CONCEPTS AND CHALLENGES

FORCE, MOTION, AND WORK

Leonard Bernstein ◆ Martin Schachter ◆ Alan Winkler ◆ Stanley Wolfe

Stanley Wolfe
Project Coordinator

GLOBE FEARON
Pearson Learning Group

The following people have contributed to the development of this product:

Art and Design: Evelyn Bauer, Susan Brorein, Tracey Gerber, Bernadette Hruby, Carol Marie Kiernan, Mindy Klarman, Judy Mahoney, Karen Mancinelli, Elbaliz Mendez, April Okano, Dan Thomas, Jennifer Visco

Editorial: Stephanie P. Cahill, Gina Dalessio, Nija Dixon, Martha Feehan, Theresa McCarthy, Maurice Sabean, Marilyn Sarch, Maury Solomon, Jeffrey Wickersty, Shirley C. White, S. Adrienn Vegh-Soti

Editorial Services: Thomas Daning, Richetta Lobban

Manufacturing: Mark Cirillo, Tom Dunne

Marketing: Douglas Falk, Maureen Christensen

Production: Irene Belinsky, Linda Bierniak, Carlos Blas, Karen Edmonds, Cheryl Golding, Leslie Greenberg, Roxanne Knoll, Susan Levine, Cynthia Lynch, Jennifer Murphy, Lisa Svoronos, Susan Tamm

Publishing Operations: Carolyn Coyle

Technology: Jessie Lin, Ellen Strain, Joanne Saito

About the Cover: Work is done when a force, a push or a pull, causes something to move in the direction of that force. The work produced by a force may be as breathtaking as the rush of a speeding roller coaster or as simple as the slow turning of gears in a complex piece of machinery.

ISBN: 0-13-024196-2

Printed in the United States of America

1 2 3 4 5 6 7 8 9 10   06 05 04 03

1-800-321-3106
www.pearsonlearning.com

Acknowledgments

Science Consultants

Jonathan Cohen
Science Teacher
Longfellow Arts and Technology
Magnet Middle School
Berkeley, California

Kenneth S. Fink
Liberty Science Center
Jersey City, New Jersey

Laboratory Consultants

Sean Devine
Science Teacher
Ridge High School
Basking Ridge, New Jersey

Vincent Dionisio
Science Teacher
Clifton High School
Clifton, New Jersey

Gregory Vogt, Ph.D.
Associate Professor, Civil Engineering
Colorado State University
Fort Collins, Colorado

Reading Consultant

Sharon Cook
Consultant
Leadership in Literacy

Internet Consultant

Janet M. Gaudino
Science Teacher
Montgomery Middle School
Skillman, New Jersey

ESL/ELL Consultant

Elizabeth Jimenez
Consultant
Pomona, California

Content Reviewers

Paul Heiney (Chs. 1, 3)
Professor of Physics
University of Pennsylvania
Philadelphia, Pennsylvania

Dr. Charles Liu (pp.. 20, 21)
Astrophysicist
Department of Astrophysics and Hayden
Planetarium
American Museum of Natural History
New York, New York

Terry Moran (pp. 94, 95)
Moran Research Service
Harvard, Massachusetts

Dr. Raymond C. Turner (Chs. 3, 4)
Alumni Distinguished Professor Emeritus of Physics
Department of Physics and Astronomy
Clemson University
Clemson, South Carolina

Todd Woerner (pp. 48, 49, 68, 69)
Department of Chemistry
Duke University
Durham, North Carolina

Teacher Reviewers

Leonard GeRue
Hanshaw Middle School
Modesto, California

Charles Sehulster
Science Teacher
Horace Greeley High School
Chappaqua, New York

Contents

Scientific Skills and Investigations Handbooks

Chapter 1 Force

Chapter 2 Motion

Features

Hands-On Activities

How Do They Know That?

◆ Integrating the Sciences

Real-Life Science

People in Science

Science and Technology

INVESTIGATE

Web InfoSearch

What are scientific skills?

People are naturally curious. They want to understand the world around them. The field of science would probably not exist if it were not for human curiosity about the natural world.

People also want to be able to make good guesses about the future. They want to know how to use alternative forms of energy. They want to improve technology and communications.

Scientists use many skills to explore the world and gather information about it. These skills are called science process skills. Another name for them is science inquiry skills.

Science process skills allow you to think like a scientist. They help you identify problems and answer questions. Sometimes they help you solve problems. More often, they provide some possible answers and lead to more questions. In this book, you will use a variety of science process skills to understand the facts and theories in physical science.

Science process skills are not only used in science. You compare prices when you shop and you observe what happens to foods when you cook them. You predict what the weather will be by looking at the sky. In fact, science process skills are really everyday life skills that have been adapted for problem solving in science.

1 NAME: What is the name for the skills scientists use to solve problems?

▲ **Figure 1** Scientists use science process skills to understand what makes a nuclear power plant run safely, how robots work in spaces too small for humans, and why communications are better using fiber optics.

Contents

1 Observing and Comparing

Making Observations An important part of solving any problem is observing, or using your senses to find out what is going on around you. The five senses are sight, hearing, touch, smell, and taste. When you look at the properties of an ore or watch an ice cube melt, you are observing. When you observe, you pay close attention to everything that happens around you.

Scientists observe the world in ways that other scientists can repeat. This is a goal of scientific observation. It is expected that when a scientist has made an observation, other people will be able to make the same observation.

▶ 2 **LIST:** What are the five senses?

Comparing and Contrasting Part of observing is comparing and contrasting. When you compare data, you observe the characteristics of several things or events to see how they are alike. When you contrast data, you look for ways that similar things are different from one another.

▲ **Figure 2** Silver and aluminum are alike in many ways. They also have many differences.

▶ 3 **COMPARE/CONTRAST:** How are a bar of aluminum and a bar of silver alike? How are they different?

Using Tools to Observe Sometimes an object is too small or too distant to see with your eyes alone. Often, special tools are needed for making observations. Sometimes scientists use tools to make observations of things like radio waves or X-rays that are outside the range of our senses. Telescopes, spectrometers, microscopes, and magnifying glasses are all examples of tools that help with scientific observations.

▲ **Figure 3** Examining a slide with a magnifying glass

▶ 4 **INFER:** What are some things that scientists might need a microscope to see?

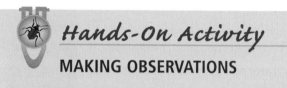

Hands-On Activity

MAKING OBSERVATIONS

You and a partner will need 2 shoeboxes with lids, 2 rubber bands, and several small objects.

1. Place several small objects into the shoebox. Do not let your partner see what you put into the shoebox.
2. Cover the shoebox with the lid. Put a rubber band around the shoebox to keep the lid on.
3. Exchange shoeboxes with your partner.
4. Gently shake, turn, and rattle the shoebox.
5. Try to describe what is in the shoebox without opening it. Write your descriptions on a sheet of paper.

Practicing Your Skills

6. **IDENTIFY:** What science process skill did you use?
7. **IDENTIFY:** Which of your senses was most important to you?
8. **ANALYZE:** Direct observation is seeing something with your eyes or hearing it with your ears. Indirect observation involves using a model or past experience to make a guess about something. Which kind of observation did you use?

2 Classifying Data

Key Term

data: information you collect when you observe something

Collecting and Classifying Data The information you collect when you observe something is called **data.** The data from an experiment or from observations you have made are first recorded, or written down. Then, they are classified.

When you classify data, you group things together based on how they are alike. This information often comes from making comparisons as you observe. You may classify by size, shape, color, use, or any other important feature. Classifying data helps you recognize and understand the relationships between things. Classification makes studying large groups of things easier. For example, physical scientists use classification to organize different types of elements.

▶ **5 EXPLAIN:** How can you classify data?

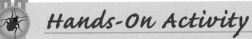

Hands-On Activity

ORGANIZING LIQUIDS

You will need 10 to 15 jars or bottles filled with a variety of liquids.

1. Carefully examine the liquids in the containers. Observe their color, thickness, and composition. Notice what happens when you gently shake the bottle. What happens when you let the liquid settle?

2. Make a system for classifying the liquids.

3. Categorize all the liquids.

4. Write a description of how you would use your classification system to classify a new liquid that you have never seen before.

Practicing Your Skills

5. **ANALYZE:** How did you classify the liquids?

6. **EXPLAIN:** Why is a classification system useful?

3 Modeling and Simulating

Key Terms

model: tool scientists use to represent an object or process

simulation: computer model that usually shows a process

Modeling Sometimes things are too small to see with your eyes alone. Other times, an object is too large to see. You may need a model to help you examine the object. A **model** is a good way to show what a very small or a very large object looks like. A model can have more details than what may be seen with just your eyes. It can be used to represent a process or an object that is hard to explain with words. A model can be a three-dimensional picture, a drawing, a computer image, or a diagram.

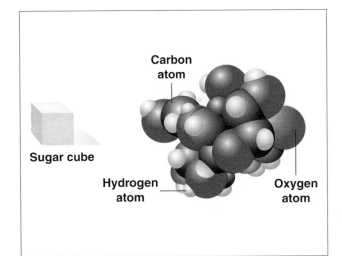

Carbon atom

Sugar cube

Hydrogen atom

Oxygen atom

▲ **Figure 4** Some schools have molecule-building kits. Each atom is color-coded according to the element it represents.

▶ **6 DEFINE:** What is a model?

Simulating A **simulation** is a kind of model that shows a process. It is often done using a computer. You can use a simulation to predict the outcome of an experiment. Scientists use simulations to study everything from chemical reactions to the global climate.

▶ **7 DEFINE:** What is a simulation?

4 Measuring

Key Terms

unit: amount used to measure something

meter: basic unit of length or distance

mass: amount of matter in something

gram: basic unit of mass

volume: amount of space an object takes up

liter: basic unit of liquid volume

meniscus: curve at the surface of a liquid in a thin tube

temperature: measure of the amount of heat energy something contains

Two Systems of Measurement When you measure, you compare an unknown value with a known value using standard units. A **unit** is an amount used to measure something. The metric system is an international system of measurement. Examples of metric units are the gram, the kilometer, and the liter. In the United States, the English system and the metric system are both used. Examples of units in the English system are the pound, the foot, and the gallon.

There is also a more modern form of the metric system called SI. The letters *SI* stand for the French words *Système International*. Many of the units in the SI are the same as those in the metric system.

The metric and SI systems are both based on units of ten. This makes them easy to use. Each unit in these systems is ten times greater than the unit before it. To show a change in the size of a unit, you add a prefix to the unit. The prefix tells you whether the unit is larger or smaller. For example, a centimeter is ten times bigger than a millimeter.

PREFIXES AND THEIR MEANINGS	
kilo-	one thousand (1,000)
hecto-	one hundred (100)
deca-	ten (10)
deci-	one-tenth (1/10)
centi-	one-hundredth (1/100)
milli-	one-thousandth (1/1,000)

◀ **Figure 5**

8▶ IDENTIFY: What are two measurement systems?

Units of Length Length is the distance from one point to another. In the metric system, the basic unit of length or distance is the **meter.** A meter is about the length from a doorknob to the floor. Longer distances, such as the distances between cities, are measured in kilometers. A kilometer is 1,000 meters. Centimeters and millimeters measure shorter distances. A centimeter is 1/100 of a meter. A millimeter is 1/1,000 of a meter. Figure 6 compares common units of length. It also shows the abbreviation for each unit.

SI/METRIC UNITS OF LENGTH	
1,000 millimeters (mm)	1 meter (m)
100 centimeters (cm)	1 meter
10 decimeters (dm)	1 meter
10 millimeters	1 centimeter
1,000 meters	1 kilometer (km)

▲ **Figure 6**

Length can be measured with a meter stick. A meter stick is 1 m long and is divided into 100 equal lengths by numbered lines. The distance between each of these lines is equal to 1 cm. Each centimeter is divided into ten equal parts. Each one of these parts is equal to 1 mm.

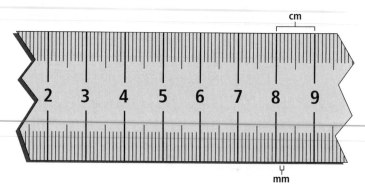

▲ **Figure 7** A meter stick is divided into centimeters and millimeters.

9▶ CALCULATE: How many centimeters are there in 3 m?

Measuring Area Do you know how people find the area of the floor of a room? They measure the length and the width of the room. Then, they multiply the two numbers. You can find the area of any rectangle by multiplying its length by its width. Area is expressed in square units, such as square meters (m²) or square centimeters (cm²).

Area = length × width

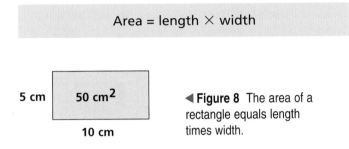

◀ **Figure 8** The area of a rectangle equals length times width.

▶10 CALCULATE: What is the area of a rectangle 12 cm by 6 cm?

Mass and Weight The amount of matter in something is its **mass.** The basic metric unit of mass is called a **gram (g).** A paper clip has about 1 g of mass. Mass is measured with an instrument called a balance. A balance works like a seesaw. It compares an unknown mass with a known mass.

One kind of balance that is commonly used to measure mass is a triple-beam balance. A triple-beam balance has a pan. The object being measured is placed on the pan. The balance also has three beams. Weights, called riders, are moved along each beam until the object on the pan is balanced. Each rider gives a reading in grams. The mass of the object is equal to the total readings of all three riders.

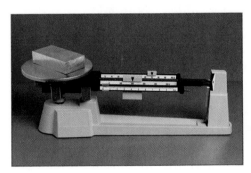

◀ **Figure 9** A triple-beam balance

Mass and weight are related; however, they are not the same. The weight of an object is a measure of Earth's pull of gravity between Earth and that object. Gravity is the force that pulls objects toward the center of Earth. The strength of the pull of gravity between two objects depends on the distance between the objects and how much mass they each contain. So, the weight of an object changes as its mass changes and as its distance from the center of Earth changes.

▶11 IDENTIFY: What instrument is used to measure mass?

Volume The amount of space an object takes up is its **volume.** You can measure the volume of liquids and solids. Liquid volume is usually measured in **liters.** Soft drinks in the United States often come in 2-liter bottles.

A graduated cylinder is used to measure liquid volume. Graduated cylinders are calibrated, or marked off, at regular intervals. Look at Figure 10. It shows a graduated cylinder. On this graduated cylinder, each small line is equal to 0.05 mL. The longer lines mark off every 0.25 mL up to 5.00 mL. However, every graduated cylinder is not marked in this manner. They come in different sizes up to 2,000 mL with different markings.

Always read the measurement at eye level. If you are using a glass graduated cylinder, you will need to read the mark on the graduated cylinder closest to the bottom of the meniscus. A **meniscus** is the curve at the surface of a liquid in a thin tube. A plastic graduated cylinder does not show a meniscus.

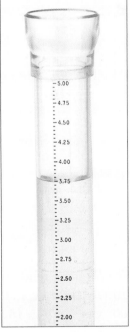

▲ **Figure 10** This glass graduated cylinder shows a meniscus.

The volume of solid objects is often measured in cubic centimeters. One cubic centimeter equals 1 mL.

Look at Figure 11. Each side of the cube is 1 cm long. The volume of the cube is 1 cubic centimeter (1 cm³). Now, look at the drawing of the box in Figure 12. Its length is 3 cm. Its width is 2 cm. Its height is 2 cm. The volume of the box can be found by multiplying length by width by height. In this case, volume equals 3 × 2 × 2. Therefore, the volume of the box is 12 cm³.

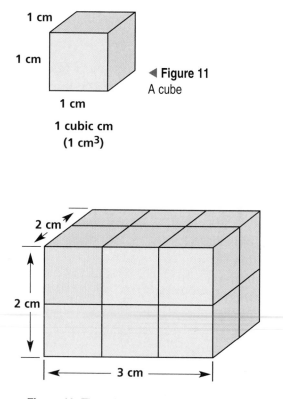

◀ **Figure 11**
A cube

1 cm

1 cm

1 cm

1 cubic cm
(1 cm³)

2 cm

2 cm

3 cm

▲ **Figure 12** The volume of a box equals length times width times height.

$$V = l \times w \times h$$

If you have a box that is 10 cm on each side, its volume would be 1,000 cm³. A liter is the same as 1,000 cm³. One liter of liquid will fill the box exactly.

12 ▶ CALCULATE: How many milliliters of water would fill a 12-cm³ box?

🐞 *Hands-On Activity*

CALCULATING AREA AND VOLUME

You will need 3 boxes of different sizes, paper, and a metric ruler.

1. Measure the length, width, and height of each box in centimeters. Record each measurement in your notes.

2. Calculate the volume of each box. Record each volume in your notes.

3. Find the surface area of each box. Record each area in your notes.

Practicing Your Skills

4. ANALYZE: Which of the three boxes has the largest volume?

5. CALCULATE: How many milliliters of liquid would fill each box?

6. ANALYZE: What is the surface area of the largest box?

Temperature **Temperature** is a measure of the amount of heat energy something contains. An instrument that measures temperature is called a thermometer.

Most thermometers are glass tubes. At the bottom of the tube is a wider part, called the bulb. The bulb is filled with liquid. Liquids that are often used include mercury, colored alcohol, or colored water. When heat is added, the liquid expands, or gets larger. It rises in the glass tube. When heat is taken away, the liquid contracts, or gets smaller. The liquid falls in the tube. On the side of the tube is a series of marks. You read the temperature by looking at the mark on the tube where the liquid stops.

Temperature can be measured on three different scales. These scales are the Fahrenheit (F) scale, the Celsius (C) scale, and the Kelvin (K) scale. The Fahrenheit scale is part of the English system of measurement. The Celsius scale is usually used in science. Almost all scientists, even in the United States, use the Celsius scale. Each unit on the Celsius scale is a degree Celsius (°C). The degree Celsius is the metric unit of temperature. Water freezes at 0°C. It boils at 100°C.

Scientists working with very low temperatures use the Kelvin scale. The Kelvin scale is part of the SI measurement system. It begins at absolute zero, or 0K. This number indicates, in theory at least, a total lack of heat.

COMPARING TEMPERATURE SCALES			
	Kelvin	Fahrenheit	Celsius
Boiling point of water	373K	212°F	100°C
Human body temperature	310K	98.6°F	37°C
Freezing point of water	273K	32°F	0°C
Absolute zero	0K	−459.67°F	−273.15°C

▲ Figure 13

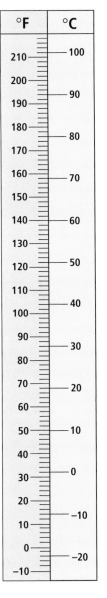

◀ Figure 14 The Fahrenheit and Celsius scales

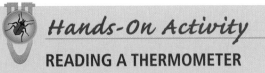

Hands-On Activity

READING A THERMOMETER

You will need safety goggles, a lab apron, 2 beakers, a heat source, ice water, a wax pencil, a ruler, and a standard Celsius thermometer.

1. Boil some water in a beaker.
   ⚠ CAUTION: Be very careful when working with heat. Place your thermometer in the beaker. Do not let the thermometer touch the sides or bottom of the beaker. Wait until the mercury rises as far as it will go. Record the temperature.

2. Fill a beaker with ice water. Place the unmarked thermometer into this beaker. Wait until the mercury goes as low as it will go. Record the temperature.

▲ STEP 1 Record the temperature of the boiling water.

Practicing Your Skills

3. IDENTIFY: What is the temperature at which the mercury rose as high as it would go?

4. IDENTIFY: What is the temperature at which the mercury went as low as it would go?

13▶ NAME: What are the three scales used to measure temperature?

5 Analyzing Data and Communicating Results

Key Term

communication: sharing information

Analyzing Data When you organize information, you put it in a logical order. In scientific experiments, it is important to organize your data. Data collected during an experiment are not very useful unless they are organized and easy to read. It is also important to organize your data if you plan to share the results of your experiment.

Scientists often organize information visually by using data tables, charts, graphs, and diagrams. By using tables, charts, graphs, and diagrams, scientists can display a lot of information in a small space. They also make it easier to compare and interpret data.

Tables are made up of rows and columns. Columns run up and down. Rows run from left to right. Tables display data in an orderly arrangement, often numerically. For example, reading a table containing the uses of sulfuric acid shows that the largest use of sulfuric acid is in fertilizers. Figure 15 is a table that shows some uses of sulfuric acid.

USES OF SULFURIC ACID	
Product	**Percentage**
Dyes, batteries, paint, explosives	15
Raw materials	15
Fertilizers	60
Petroleum refining	5
Metal processing	5

▲ Figure 15

Graphs, such as bar graphs, line graphs, and circle graphs, often use special coloring, shading, or patterns to represent information. Keys indicate what the special markings represent. Line graphs have horizontal (x) and vertical (y) axes to indicate such things as time and quantities.

14 EXPLAIN: How do tables and graphs help you analyze data?

Sharing Results When you talk to a friend, you are communicating, or sharing information. If you write a letter or a report, you are also communicating but in a different way. Scientists communicate all the time. They communicate to share results, information, and opinions. They write books and magazine or newspaper articles. They may also create Web sites about their work. This is called written **communication.**

Graphs are a visual way to communicate. The circle graph in Figure 16 is showing the same information that is shown in Figure 15. The circle graph presents the information in a different way.

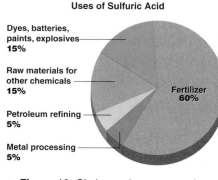

Uses of Sulfuric Acid

Dyes, batteries, paints, explosives 15%

Raw materials for other chemicals 15%

Petroleum refining 5%

Metal processing 5%

Fertilizer 60%

▲ **Figure 16** Circle graphs are a good way to show parts of a whole.

15 LIST: What are some ways to communicate the results of an experiment?

6 Making Predictions

Key Terms

infer: to form a conclusion

predict: to state ahead of time what you think is going to happen

Thinking of Possibilities When you **infer** something, you form a conclusion. This is called making an inference. Your conclusion will usually be based on observations or past experience. You may use logic to form your statement. Your statement might be supported by evidence and perhaps can be tested by an experiment. An inference is not a fact. It is only one possible explanation.

When you **predict,** you state ahead of time what you think will happen. Predictions about future events are based on inferences, evidence, or past experience. The two science process skills of inferring and predicting are very closely related.

16 CONTRAST: What is the difference between inferring and predicting?

How do you conduct a scientific investigation?

By now, you should have a good understanding of the science process skills. These skills are used to solve many science problems. There is also a basic procedure, or plan, that scientists usually follow when conducting investigations. Some people call this procedure the scientific method.

The scientific method is a series of steps that can serve as a guide to solving problems or answering questions. It uses many of the science process skills you know, such as observing and predicting.

Not all experiments use all of the steps in the scientific method. Some experiments follow all of them, but in a different order. In fact, there is no one right scientific method. Each problem is different. Some problems may require steps that another problem would not. However, most investigations will follow the same basic procedure.

1 DESCRIBE: What is the scientific method?

▲ Figure 1 Scientists use the scientific method to guide experiments.

Contents

1 Identifying a Problem and Doing Research

Starting an Investigation Scientists often state a problem as a question. This is the first step in a scientific investigation. Most experiments begin by asking a scientific question. That is, they ask a question that can be answered by gathering evidence. This question is the reason for the scientific investigation. It also helps determine how the investigation will proceed.

Have you ever done background research for a science project? When you do this kind of research, you are looking for data that others have already obtained on the same subject. You can gather research by reading books, magazines, and newspapers, and by using the Internet to find out what other scientists have done. Doing research is the first step of gathering evidence for a scientific investigation.

▶ **2 IDENTIFY:** What is the first step of a scientific investigation?

BUILDING SCIENCE SKILLS

Researching Background Information Suppose you notice that the brown paper towels at school do not seem to soak up as much water as the paper towels used in your home. You wonder which kinds of paper towels absorb, or soak up, the most water. You wonder if there is a connection between the paper towels' thickness and absorbency.

To determine which paper towels are most absorbent, look for information on paper towels in magazines, in books, or on the Internet. Put your findings in a report.

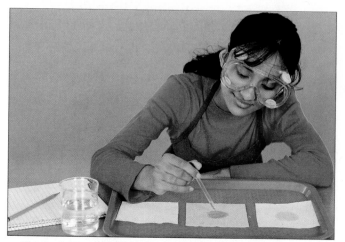
▲ **Figure 2** Testing paper towels for absorbency

2 Forming a Hypothesis

Key Terms

hypothesis: suggested answer to a question or problem

theory: set of hypotheses that have been supported by testing over and over again

Focusing the Investigation Scientists usually state clearly what they expect to find out in an investigation. This is called stating a hypothesis. A **hypothesis** is a suggested answer to a question or a solution to a problem. Stating a hypothesis helps to keep you focused on the problem and helps you decide what to test.

To form their hypotheses, scientists must think of possible explanations for a set of observations or they must suggest possible answers to a scientific question. One of those explanations becomes the hypothesis. In science, a hypothesis must include something that can be tested.

A hypothesis is more than just a guess. It must consider observations, past experiences, and previous knowledge. It is an inference turned into a statement that can be tested. A set of hypotheses that have been supported by testing over and over again by many scientists is called a **theory.** An example is the theory that explains how living things have evolved, or changed, over time.

A hypothesis can take the form of an "if . . . then" statement. A well-worded hypothesis is a guide for how to set up and perform an experiment.

▶ **3 DESCRIBE:** How does a scientist form a hypothesis?

BUILDING SCIENCE SKILLS

Developing a Hypothesis A hypothesis for an experiment about which paper towels absorb the most water might be stated as follows:

If thicker paper towels soak up more water than thin paper towels, then thickness is an important factor for paper towel absorbency.

However, what do you mean by thicker? Are the paper towels really different? Does color or design make a difference? You need to make your hypothesis specific. Revise the hypothesis above to make it more specific.

3 Designing and Carrying Out an Experiment

Key Terms

variable: anything that can affect the outcome of an experiment

constant: something that does not change

controlled experiment: experiment in which all the conditions except one are kept constant

Testing the Hypothesis Scientists need to plan how to test their hypotheses. This means they must design an experiment. The plan must be a step-by-step procedure. It should include a record of any observations made or measurements taken.

All experiments must take variables into account. A **variable** is anything that can affect the outcome of an experiment. Room temperature, amount of sunlight, and water vapor in the air are just some of the many variables that could affect the outcome of an experiment.

▶ **4 DEFINE:** What is a variable?

Controlling the Experiment One of the variables in an experiment should be what you are testing. This is what you will change during the experiment. All other variables need to remain the same. In this experiment, you will vary the type of paper towel.

A **constant** is something that does not change. If there are no constants in your experiment, you will not be sure why you got the results you did. An experiment in which all the conditions except one are kept constant is called a **controlled experiment.**

Some experiments have two setups. In one setup, called the control, nothing is changed. In the other setup, the variable being tested is changed. Later, the control group can be compared with the other group to provide useful data.

▶ **5 EXPLAIN:** Explain how a controlled experiment is set up.

Designing the Procedure Suppose you want to design an experiment to determine if a paper towel's thickness affects its absorbency. You decide to do a set of measurements to find out the absorbency of three kinds of paper towels in a controlled environment. You will measure the thickness of the paper towels and then determine how much water each paper towel soaks up to see if your hypothesis is correct.

In designing your experiment, you need to identify the variables. The three kinds of paper towels are all variables that could effect the outcome of your experiment. Everything about testing the effect of thickness on absorbency needs to be the same except the actual thickness of each paper towel.

Finally, you should decide on the data you will collect. How will you measure the thickness of the paper towels? In this case, you might want to record the thickness of each towel, its color, whether it absorbed water, and how much water was absorbed.

The hands-on activity on page 12 is one possible experiment you could have designed. It has one method for measuring the absorbency of the paper towels. Sometimes scientists try to measure the same thing two different ways to be sure the test is accurate. Can you think of another method to measure the absorbency of paper towels?

▶ **6 LIST:** How do constants and variables affect an experiment?

Hands-On Activity

CARRYING OUT AN EXPERIMENT

You will need 3 or more kinds of paper towels, a metric ruler, an eyedropper or pipette (preferably calibrated in millimeters), and water.

1. Get three different kinds of paper towels. To find the thickness of each kind of towel, measure the thickness of five towels and divide the result by five. Set up a data table for the information you gather.

2. Now you are ready to compare the absorbency of the paper towels. Cut the paper towels into squares of equal sizes. Squares that are 10 cm in size are good for testing.

3. Lay a square of paper towel on a tray or other nonabsorbent surface. Add drops of water one at a time until the paper towel has soaked up all the water it can. Record how much water was absorbed. If your eyedropper is not marked in milliliters, you can record your data in "drops." If it is marked, then you should record the milliliters.

4. Test all the paper towel samples the exact same way. Be sure that you only measure the water that is absorbed and that you let each paper towel sample soak up as much water as it will hold.

5. You are now ready to compare your data and see if they support your hypothesis.

Practicing Your Skills

6. **OBSERVE:** What happened in the experiment? How much water did each paper towel sample absorb?

7. **COMPARE:** Which paper towel absorbed the most?

8. **EXPLAIN:** What procedures did you follow to make sure the paper towels were all given a fair and equal test?

9. **IDENTIFY:** What is the variable being tested in this experiment?

4 Recording and Analyzing Data

Dealing With Data During an experiment, you must keep careful notes about what you observe. For example, you might need to note any special steps you took in setting up the experiment, exactly how you made the drops the same size each time, or the temperature of the water. This is important information that might affect your conclusion.

At the end of an experiment, you will need to study the data to find any patterns. Much of the data you will deal with is written text. You may read a report or a summary of an experiment. However, scientific information is often a set of numbers or facts presented in other, more visual ways. These visual presentations make the information more meaningful and easier to understand. Tables, charts, and graphs, for instance, help you understand a collection of facts on a topic.

After your data have been organized, you need to ask what the data show. Do they support your hypothesis? Do they show something wrong in your experiment? Do you need to gather more data by performing another experiment?

▶ **7 LIST:** What are some ways to display data?

BUILDING SCIENCE SKILLS

Analyzing Data You made the following notes during your experiment. How would you display this information?

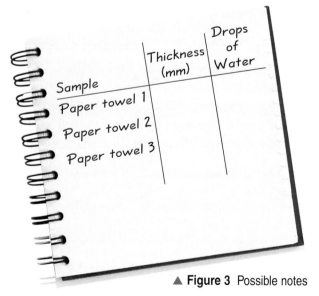

▲ **Figure 3** Possible notes

5 Stating a Conclusion

Drawing Conclusions A conclusion is a statement that sums up what you have learned from an experiment. When you draw a conclusion, you need to decide whether the data you collected supported your hypothesis. You may need to repeat an experiment several times before you can draw any conclusions from it. Conclusions often lead you to ask new questions and plan new experiments to answer them.

8 EXPLAIN: Why might it be necessary to repeat an experiment?

BUILDING SCIENCE SKILLS

Stating a Conclusion Review your hypothesis statement regarding the effect of the thickness of a paper towel on its absorbency. Then, review the data you obtained during your experiment.

- Was your hypothesis correct? Use your observations to support your answer.
- Which paper towel absorbed the most? Was it also the thickest?

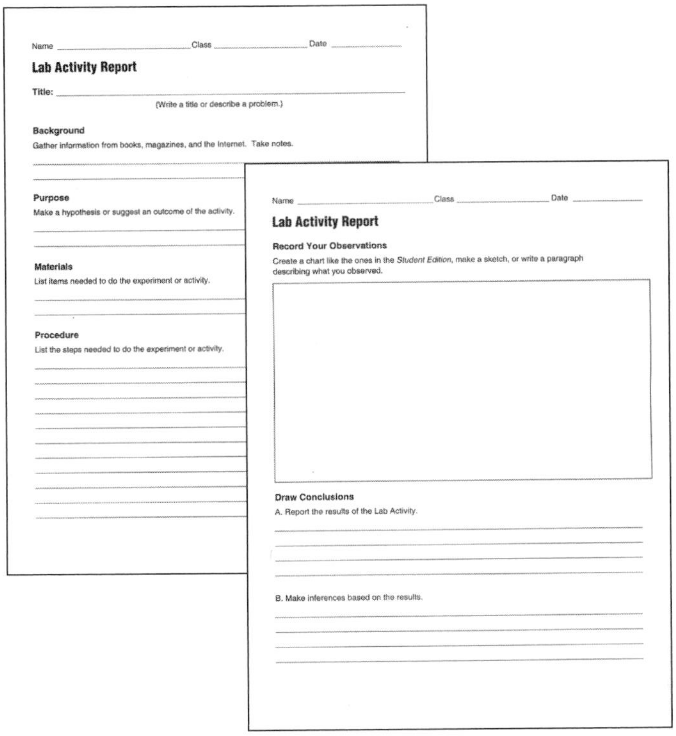
Name ____ Class ____ Date ____

Lab Activity Report

Title: ____
(Write a title or describe a problem.)

Background
Gather information from books, magazines, and the Internet. Take notes.

Purpose
Make a hypothesis or suggest an outcome of the activity.

Materials
List items needed to do the experiment or activity.

Procedure
List the steps needed to do the experiment or activity.

Name ____ Class ____ Date ____

Lab Activity Report

Record Your Observations
Create a chart like the ones in the *Student Edition*, make a sketch, or write a paragraph describing what you observed.

Draw Conclusions
A. Report the results of the Lab Activity.

B. Make inferences based on the results.

▲ **Figure 4** Throughout this program, you may use forms like these to organize your lab reports.

6 Writing a Report

Communicating Results Scientists keep careful written records of their observations and findings. These records are used to create a lab report. Lab reports are a form of written communication. They explain what happened in the experiment. A good lab report should be written so that anyone reading it can duplicate the experiment. It should contain the following information:

- A title
- A purpose
- Background information
- Your hypothesis
- Materials used
- Your step-by-step procedure
- Your observations
- Your recorded data
- Your analysis of the data
- Your conclusions

Your conclusions should relate back to the questions you asked in the "purpose" section of your report. Also, the report should not have any experimental errors that might have caused unexpected results. For example, did you follow the steps in the correct order? Did an unexpected variable interfere with your results? Was your equipment clean and in good working order? This explanation of possible errors should also be part of your conclusions.

9 EXPLAIN: Why is it important to explain possible errors in your lab report?

BUILDING SCIENCE SKILLS

Writing a Lab Report Write a lab report to communicate to other scientists your discoveries about the effect of a paper towel's thickness on its water absorbency. Your lab report should include a title, your hypothesis statement, a list of materials you used, the procedure, your observations, and your conclusions. Try to include one table of data in your report.

LAB SAFETY

Working in a science laboratory can be both exciting and meaningful. However, you must always be aware of safety precautions when carrying out experiments. There are a few basic rules that should be followed in any science laboratory:

- Read all instructions carefully before the start of an experiment. Follow all instructions exactly and in the correct order.

- Check your equipment to make sure it is clean and working properly.

- Never taste, smell, or touch any substance in the lab that you are not told to do so. Never eat or drink anything in the lab. Do not chew gum.

- Never work alone. Tell a teacher at once if an accident occurs.

Experiments that use chemicals or heat can be dangerous. The following list of rules and symbols will help you avoid accidents. There are also rules about what to do if an accident does occur. Here are some rules to remember when working in a lab:

1. Do not use glass that is chipped or metal objects with broken edges. Do not try to clean up broken glassware yourself. Notify your teacher if a piece of glassware is broken.

2. Do not use electrical cords with loose plugs or frayed ends. Do not let electrical cords cross in front of working areas. Do not use electrical equipment near water.

3. Be very careful when using sharp objects such as scissors, knives, or tweezers. Always cut in a direction away from your body.

4. Be careful when you are using a heat source. Use proper equipment, such as tongs or a ringstand, when handling hot objects.

5. Confine loose clothing and hair when working with an open flame. Be sure you know the location of the nearest fire extinguisher. Never reach across an open flame.

6. Be careful when working with poisonous or toxic substances. Never mix chemicals without directions from your teacher. Remove any long jewelry that might hang down and end up in chemicals. Avoid touching your eyes or mouth when working with these chemicals.

7. Use extreme care when working with acids and bases. Never mix acids and bases without direction from your teacher. Never smell anything directly. Use caution when handling chemicals that produce fumes.

8. Wear safety goggles, especially when working with an open flame, chemicals, and any liquids.

9. Wear lab aprons when working with substances of any sort, especially chemicals.

10. Use caution when handling or collecting plants. Some plants can be harmful if they are touched or eaten.

11. Use caution when handling live animals. Some animals can injure you or spread disease. Handle all live animals as humanely as possible.

12. Dispose of all equipment and materials properly. Keep your work area clean at all times.

13. Always wash your hands thoroughly with soap and water after handling chemicals or live organisms.

14. Follow the CAUTION and safety symbols you see used throughout this book when doing labs or other activities.

Chapter 1 Force

▲ **Figure 1-1** An electromagnet at work

The machine shown in Figure 1-1 uses magnetic force to lift and move car bodies and other large metal objects. If you have ever had to push a car, you know how much force is needed to move the car. Now think about the amount of force the machine can exert. The best part is that, unlike a permanent magnet, the magnetic force applied by the machine is supplied by electricity and can be turned on and off.

►Can you name other machines that use force to move things?

Contents

1-1 What is a force?

Objectives

Define force and give some examples of forces in nature. Identify balanced and unbalanced forces and describe their effects.

Key Terms

force: a push or a pull

balanced forces: forces that are equal in size but opposite in direction

unbalanced forces: forces that cause a change in the motion of an object

Force A **force** is a push or a pull. To open a door, you have to push or pull the door. In other words, you have to exert a force on the door. A force always acts in some direction. When you push on a door, the force is in the direction of the push. When you pull on a doorknob, the force is in the direction of the pull. If the force is strong enough, the door will move in the direction of the force.

▶ **DEFINE:** What is force?

Balanced Forces To describe a force, you must know two things—the size of the force and the direction of the force. For example, think about two teams in a tug of war. Each team pulls with equal force in opposite directions, as shown in Figure 1-2. Neither team can make the other move.

Forces that are equal in size and opposite in direction are called **balanced forces.** As the name suggests, balanced forces acting on an object do not cause a change in the motion of the object.

▶ **PREDICT:** What effect will balanced forces have on a book?

Unbalanced Forces Look at Figure 1-3. A member of one team has fallen and let go of the rope. One team now pulls harder than the other, and the rope moves. The forces acting on the rope are no longer balanced. **Unbalanced forces** cause a change in the motion of an object.

▲ **Figure 1-3** Unbalanced forces

▶ **IDENTIFY:** What kinds of forces cause an object to move?

Forces and Motion Unbalanced forces can change the motion of an object in two ways.

- When unbalanced forces act on an object at rest, the object will move.

- When unbalanced forces act on a moving object, the motion of the object will change. The object may speed up, slow down, stop moving, or change direction.

▶ **PREDICT:** What might happen when unbalanced forces act on a moving car?

▲ **Figure 1-2** Balanced forces

Forces in Nature You experience many different kinds of forces every day. A few examples of these forces are described here.

- How much do you weigh? The weight of an object is a measure of the force of gravity acting between Earth and the object.

- The attraction of a magnet for a paper clip is an example of a magnetic force.

- A kite flies in the air as a result of wind pushing against it. The force of the wind results from the moving air pushing against the kite.

- The force of falling water in a waterfall is caused by Earth's gravity acting on the water.

5 IDENTIFY: What force causes a rock to roll down the side of a mountain?

1. A _____ is a push or a pull.
2. To describe a force, you must know the size and _____ of the force.
3. Balanced forces are equal in size and _____ in direction.
4. Unbalanced forces cause a change in the _____ of an object.
5. The weight of an object is a measure of the force of _____ acting on it.
6. The force of the _____ is produced by moving air.

THINKING CRITICALLY

7. **INFER:** Describe the two forces that act on a flying kite.

Hands-On Activity

INTERPRETING FORCE DIAGRAMS

You will need a metric ruler.

1. Look at Figure 1-4. The arrow represents the force used to push a desk across the floor. Use a metric ruler to measure the length of the arrow.

2. Look at Figure 1-5. It shows a second force helping to push the desk. Measure the total length of the two arrows.

3. Look at Figure 1-6. It shows a force pushing in the opposite direction. Measure the length of the arrow pointing in the opposite direction.

Practicing Your Skills

4. **CALCULATE:** Force is measured in newtons (N). If 1 cm = 1 N, what force was used to push the desk in Figure 1-4?

5. **CALCULATE:** What was the total force used to push the desk in Figure 1-5?

6. **CALCULATE:** Look at Figure 1-6. **a.** What force was used to push the desk in the opposite direction? **b.** Subtract that force from the result in question 5 to find the total force acting on the desk.

▲ Figure 1-4

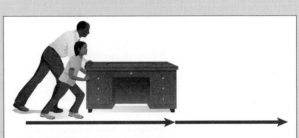

▲ Figure 1-5

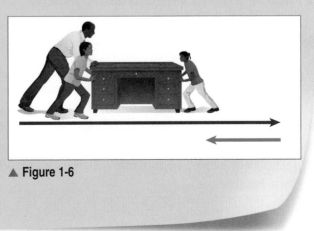

▲ Figure 1-6

1-2 What is gravity?

Sir Isaac Newton Isaac Newton was a famous scientist. He was born in England over 350 years ago. Newton wondered why all objects fall to the ground. He hypothesized that there is a force that makes all objects move toward each other. This force is gravity. All objects in the universe are attracted to one another because of the force of gravity between them. This idea is now known as Newton's law of gravity, or universal gravitation.

▲ **Figure 1-7** A falling apple provided Newton's "inspiration."

1 NAME: What scientific law explains why objects fall?

Gravity Gravity is a force of attraction between all objects in the universe. On Earth, all objects fall toward the center of Earth's mass. An apple falls to the ground because it is pulled by Earth's gravity. In fact, every object near Earth's surface is pulled toward Earth's center.

2 DESCRIBE: In which direction does an object fall on Earth?

Gravity and Mass The amount of gravitational force between two objects depends on the mass of each object. Earth's mass appears to be concentrated in Earth's center. When an apple falls from a tree, the gravitational force between Earth and the apple tends to pull them toward each other. However, because Earth has much more mass than the apple, Earth does not seem to move at all.

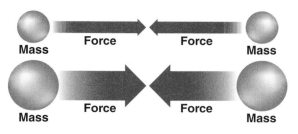

▲ **Figure 1-8** Larger masses exert greater gravitational force.

3 EXPLAIN: Why is the force of Earth's gravity so strong?

Gravity and Distance The force of gravity between two objects decreases as the distance between them increases. When you stand on Earth at sea level, the amount of gravitational force you feel is your weight. If you were far away from Earth, the gravitational force between you and Earth would be less. The force of gravity decreases by an amount equal to one divided by the distance (d) squared, or $1/d^2$. For example, if the moon were twice as far from Earth, the force of gravity between Earth and the Moon would be $1/2^2$ or 1/4 of its present value.

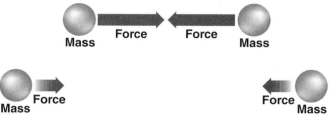

▲ **Figure 1-9** Gravitational force decreases as distance increases.

4 CALCULATE: If you were twice as far from Earth's center as you are now, how much would you weigh?

1. The idea of universal gravitation was suggested by _____.

2. All objects in the universe are attracted to each other because of the force of _____.

3. Near Earth's surface, all objects fall in the direction of Earth's _____.

4. The farther away you are from Earth, the _____ you weigh.

5. Gravity between two objects decreases as the distance between the objects _____.

THINKING CRITICALLY

6. **ANALYZE:** Why does an apple fall toward Earth, instead of Earth moving toward the apple?

7. **INFER:** The Moon travels in an orbit around Earth. What force keeps the Moon from flying off into space?

INTERPRETING VISUALS

Look at the three pairs of masses labeled a, b, and c shown in Figure 1-10.

8. Compare the forces of gravity acting between each pair of spheres and tell how you reached your conclusion.

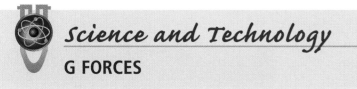

a.

b.

c.

▲ **Figure 1-10** Compare mass, distance, and gravitational force.

Science and Technology

G FORCES

Gravity pulls your body toward Earth's center. You feel that pull as your weight. Pilots and astronauts refer to this force as 1 G. Sometimes you may have the sensation of having more or less than 1 G of force on your body. For example, as you plunge down the first hill of a roller coaster, your body lifts up off the seat. This action is caused by the fact that the seat is moving down away from you. When you reach the bottom and start up the next hill, your seat pushes up against you. This action makes it feel as if you are being pushed down into your seat. These sensations are due to changing forces on your body.

▲ **Figure 1-11** As this pilot turns, he feels increased G forces.

During flight, test pilots experience much greater changes in forces. The human body cannot withstand more than 9 Gs of force. As forces increase, blood is forced from the brain and the heart cannot pump it back quickly enough. After a short time, a person loses consciousness.

To deal with increased forces, pilots wear special suits. Tubes along the sides of these suits inflate, preventing the blood from rushing from the brain.

Thinking Critically What might happen to a pilot that experienced more than 9 Gs of force during a flight maneuver?

THE Big IDEA

What keeps planets and satellites in their orbits?

The great physicist Albert Einstein liked to do something he called thinking physics. He performed thought experiments to try out new ideas in his imagination. Sometimes he did this before doing mathematical proofs or calculations. Let's try a thought experiment to visualize the forces keeping planets and satellites in orbit.

Imagine that Earth has no atmosphere, so there will be no air resistance to slow the ball down in this experiment. You are standing on top of a very tall mountain as shown in the figure on the right. You throw a ball straight out, parallel to the ground. The harder you throw the ball, the farther the ball travels before hitting the ground. The falling ball traces a curved path as it is pulled by Earth's gravity. The more force you use to throw the ball, the longer the curve.

Because there is no air resistance, if the ball is thrown hard enough, its curved falling-path matches the curve of Earth's surface. So the ball will fall continuously without hitting Earth. It will be in orbit. It is falling without reaching the ground.

Orbit happens when the velocity of an object is such that the forward motion of the object keeps the object from falling directly toward a surface. The object travels in a circular or elliptical path. When a planet orbits the Sun, it is pulled toward the Sun's surface by the powerful force of gravity between the planet and the Sun. However, the forward motion of the planet is great enough to keep the planet from falling straight to the Sun's surface. Instead, the planet goes around the Sun.

Look at the illustrations that appear on these two pages. Then, follow the directions in the Science Log to find out more about "the big idea." ✦

Earth "Falling" Around The Sun

The Sun's gravitational force pulls Earth toward the center of the Sun. However, the forward motion of Earth is equal to its motion toward the Sun, and Earth remains in an orbital path around the Sun.

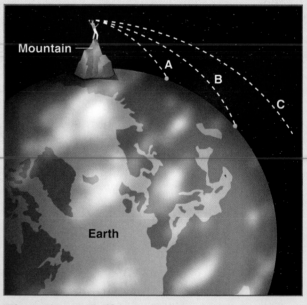

Throwing a Ball into Orbit

A ball thrown straight out from a very high mountain peak would follow a curved path (A and B) as it fell to Earth's surface. If it were thrown hard enough, its forward motion will be equal to its downward motion. This ball (C) would go into orbit around Earth.

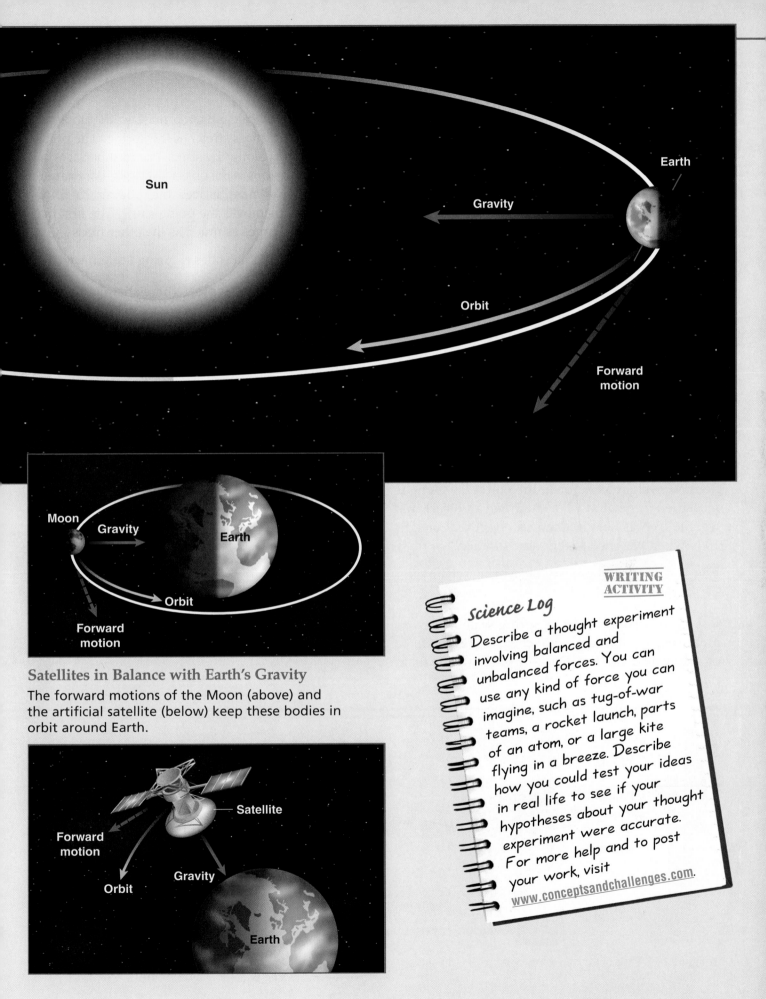

Satellites in Balance with Earth's Gravity

The forward motions of the Moon (above) and the artificial satellite (below) keep these bodies in orbit around Earth.

WRITING ACTIVITY

Science Log

Describe a thought experiment involving balanced and unbalanced forces. You can use any kind of force you can imagine, such as tug-of-war teams, a rocket launch, parts of an atom, or a large kite flying in a breeze. Describe how you could test your ideas in real life to see if your hypotheses about your thought experiment were accurate. For more help and to post your work, visit www.conceptsandchallenges.com.

1-3 How does a spring scale work?

Objective

Describe how a spring scale is used to measure weight.

Key Term

newton: SI unit of force

The SI Unit of Force There are different SI units for different types of measurements. For example, the basic unit of distance is the meter (m). The basic unit of mass is the kilogram (kg). The **newton** (N) is the basic SI unit of force. The unit is named in honor of Sir Isaac Newton. On Earth, it takes a force equal to 9.8 N to lift a 1-kg mass.

Weight is a familiar example of force. An object's weight is a measure of the force of gravity acting on the object. When you weigh an object, you measure the pull of gravity on the object. Because weight is a force, an object's weight is measured in newtons. For example, an object that weighs 15 N is heavier than an object that weighs 10 N when weighed at the same location.

 IDENTIFY: What are you measuring when you weigh an object?

Using a Spring Scale A spring scale is used to measure weight. A spring scale measures the force of gravity on an object. Figure 1-12 shows the main parts of a spring scale.

To use the scale, attach a mass to the hook. The weight of the mass stretches the spring. The pointer moves down along the scale. The number at which the pointer stops is the object's weight. For example, suppose one mass moves the pointer to 5, and another mass moves the pointer to 1. The first mass weighs five times as much as the other mass.

2 IDENTIFY: What does a spring scale measure?

Types of Spring Scales There are many types of spring scales. The scale shown in Figure 1-12 is similar to the type of spring scale used in a science lab. Many bathroom scales are also spring scales. When you stand on the scale, your weight pushes on a spring. The spring causes a circular scale to turn until the number on the scale lines up with the pointer. This number shows your weight.

Another type of spring scale is the one you see in the fruit and vegetable section of a market. If you place some grapes or apples on the scale, the weight of the fruit pulls a spring. The spring turns the pointer to show the weight of the fruit.

▲ **Figure 1-13** A grocer's scale can weigh fruits and vegetables.

3 LIST: What are three types of spring scales?

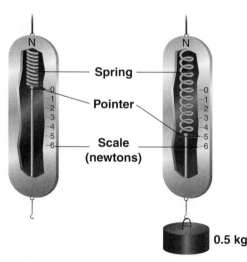

0.5 kg

▲ **Figure 1-12** Parts of a spring scale

Spring
Pointer
Scale (newtons)

☑ CHECKING CONCEPTS

1. The SI unit of force is the _____.
2. Weight is a _____ measured in newtons.
3. The greater the mass of an object the _____ its weight will be.
4. A spring scale is used to measure _____.
5. A bathroom scale is a kind of _____.

💡 THINKING CRITICALLY

6. INFER: It takes 10 N to lift an object. What is the object's weight? How do you know?
7. IDENTIFY: What force is being measured when you use a spring scale to measure weight?
8. CALCULATE: One object causes the spring of a scale to stretch four times farther than a second object. If the second object weighs 3 N, what is the weight of the first object?

Web InfoSearch

Bathroom Scale Have you ever wondered how your bathroom scale is able to measure over 200 pounds while being so thin and small? Most bathroom scales use spring scales like those found in supermarkets. However, bathroom scales use ratios to allow smaller, less powerful springs to accurately measure heavier weights.

SEARCH: Use the Internet to find out how a bathroom scale works. What is a ratio? How is a bathroom scale able to use a small spring to measure heavy weights? Start your search at www.conceptsandchallenges.com. Some key search words are **how bathroom scale works, inside bathroom scale,** and **bathroom spring scale.**

⚛ Hands-On Activity

USING A SPRING SCALE

You will need a spring scale, a small mass, and several small objects.

1. Be sure that the pointer of the spring scale is at zero when nothing is hanging from it.
2. Carefully place a mass on the hook of the spring scale. Do not let the mass drop. This might damage the spring scale.
3. Observe where the pointer stops on the scale. If the pointer stops between two numbers, round the number to the nearest half. Record your measurement.
4. Use the spring scale to weigh several small objects. Record and compare your measurements.

▲ STEP 2 Place a mass on the hook.

Practicing Your Skills

5. ANALYZE: What force are you measuring when you weigh an object?
6. COMPARE: How much does a 1-kg mass weigh in newtons?
7. OBSERVE: In newtons, what are the weights of the masses measured in the activity?

1-4 What is friction?

Forces and Motion To stop a moving object, a force must act in the direction opposite to the direction of motion. If you give your book a push across your desk, the book will move. The force of the push moves the book. As the book slides across the desk, it slows down and stops moving.

 OBSERVE: Give your textbook a slight push across your desk. What must you do to keep the book moving?

Friction A force that opposes the motion of an object is called **friction.** Look at Figure 1-14. At first, the book is at rest. A push (F) causes the book to start sliding across the desk. As the book slides across the desk, a force of friction (f) acts in the opposite direction. The friction slows the motion of the book. Finally, the book is once again at rest.

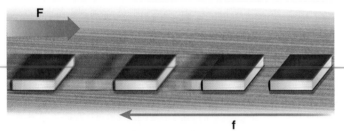

▲ **Figure 1-14** What force slows the moving book?

 DEFINE: What is friction?

Types of Friction There are different types of friction. A book sitting on a desk has static friction. This is the force that must be overcome to start the book moving. A book moving across the desk is an example of sliding friction. As the book slides across the desk, the bottom of the book is touching the desk. The source of the friction is the contact between the surface of the book and the desk. Air resistance is a type of friction. As an object falls, air resistance pushes up on the object. When you ride a bicycle, the contact between the tires and the road is an example of rolling friction.

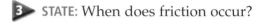 **STATE:** When does friction occur?

Useful Friction On Earth, friction makes motion possible. When you ride a bicycle, the friction between the road and the bicycle wheels is necessary to keep the bicycle in motion. Without friction, you would not be able to stop the bicycle. You would not be able to climb a rope, throw a ball, or even walk down the street. Pencils would not work, and kites, birds, and airplanes would not be able to fly. As you can see, life without friction would be very different and very difficult.

▲ **Figure 1-15** Drag racers depend on friction between their tires and the track.

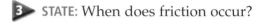 **LIST:** Name several activities that would not be possible without friction.

Harmful Friction Sometimes friction is not helpful. For example, think about trying to ski down a hill covered with grass instead of snow. You might be able to do it, but friction between the grass and the skis would make it a slow, bumpy ride.

Unwanted friction can also be found in machines and engines. Many machines have moving metal parts that touch. The rubbing together of these parts produces heat and can cause parts to wear out.

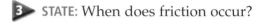 **EXPLAIN:** Why is it sometimes useful to reduce friction?

☑ CHECKING CONCEPTS

1. A book sliding across a desk will come to a stop because of the force of _____.

2. A book sliding across a desk is an example of _____ friction.

3. The type of friction that acts on an object falling through the atmosphere is called _____.

4. Friction makes _____ possible.

💡 THINKING CRITICALLY

5. INFER: When a car's tires are stuck in snow or mud, is it better to have more or less friction? Why?

6. HYPOTHESIZE: Sand is often placed on top of ice on roads and highways. Why do you think the sand is used?

7. CLASSIFY: Decide which of the following is an example of sliding friction, rolling friction, or air resistance. **a.** an airplane descending **b.** a person roller-skating **c.** a person ice skating **d.** a falling leaf

8. CALCULATE: Copy the diagram in Figure 1-16 onto a sheet of paper. A force of 10 N is causing the object to slide across a tabletop from left to right. There is a 3-N force of friction opposing that motion. Complete the diagram, using arrows to show all the forces acting on the object.

▲ **Figure 1-16** Complete the diagram.

⚛ *Hands-On Activity*

MEASURING FRICTION

You will need a spring scale, a small object, a long sheet of sandpaper, and tape.

1. Place the small object on a tabletop. Attach the spring scale to the object. Pull the object across the table at a constant speed. Record the amount of force shown on the spring scale.

2. The force measured in Step 1 is the force of friction on the object from the tabletop.

3. Repeat Steps 1 to 3. This time use the sheet of sandpaper. Tape the sandpaper to the tabletop. Use the spring scale to pull the object across the sandpaper at the same speed as before.

Practicing Your Skills

4. OBSERVE: What was the force of friction on the object from the tabletop?

5. OBSERVE: What was the force of friction on the object from the sandpaper?

6. INFER: Does a smooth surface offer less friction or more friction than a rough surface?

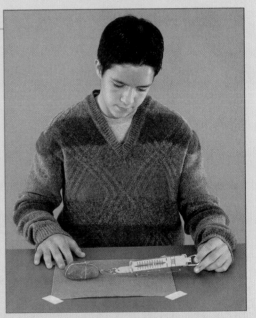

▲ **STEP 3** Pull the object across the sandpaper with the spring scale.

1-5 How can friction be changed?

Objective
Describe some ways to change friction.

Key Term
lubricants (LOO-brih-kuhnts): materials that reduce friction

Moving Against Friction Friction makes it hard to move objects. Force is needed to overcome the force of friction. Suppose you wanted to push a heavy wooden box across the floor. As you push against the box, sliding friction equal to a force of 5 N pushes in the opposite direction. This means that it will take a total force greater than 5 N to push the box.

▲ **Figure 1-17** Overcoming sliding friction

1 CALCULATE: If the force of friction is 16 N, how much force is needed to move the object?

Using Rolling Friction Reducing friction makes it easier to move an object. One way to reduce friction is to change sliding friction to rolling friction. When you try to push a wooden box across a floor, you have to overcome sliding friction. The size of this frictional force depends on the types of surfaces in contact with each other. In this case, the bottom of the box is in contact with the floor. If you put the box on a wheeled cart, there will be much less friction. Rolling friction is always less than sliding friction. With the box on wheels, you use less force to push the box.

▲ **Figure 1-18** Using rolling friction

2 EXPLAIN: Why must you reduce friction in order to move certain objects?

Using Lubricants You can also reduce friction by using lubricants. **Lubricants** are materials that reduce friction. For example, in a car's engine, metal parts called pistons are in contact with other metal parts. When two pieces of metal touch, there is a lot of friction. Oil is used to reduce the friction between the metal parts. Oil is a lubricant. It separates the metal parts from one another. Without the oil, the metal parts would scrape against one another. This would make the engine overheat and wear out more quickly.

3 IDENTIFY: When would it be helpful to use a lubricant?

Not Enough Friction Have you ever slipped on an icy sidewalk or seen a car skid out of control? These things happen when there is not enough friction between surfaces such as your feet and the ice or the tires and the road. In such cases, it is necessary to increase friction. This can be done by spreading sand on an icy surface or using tires with a deeper tread.

Athletes often wear special footwear to increase friction between their feet and the surfaces over which they move. Basketball players wear shoes with soles designed not to slip on a hardwood floor. In several sports, players wear shoes with spiked soles to give their feet a better grip on the ground.

▲ **Figure 1-19** Sometimes it helps to increase friction.

4 HYPOTHESIZE: Why do staircases often have rubber mats on the steps?

 CHECKING CONCEPTS

1. Because of friction, it takes _____ force to move an object.

2. When friction is _____ , it is easier to move an object.

3. Waxing a floor makes the floor slippery because wax is a _____.

4. If you wear roller skates instead of shoes, you _____ the friction between your feet and the floor.

THINKING CRITICALLY

5. ANALYZE: Is it easier to push a heavy object across a carpeted floor or across a polished wooden floor? Why?

6. CALCULATE: Find the amount of force in each example. **a.** If it takes 20 N to slide a wooden crate across the floor, what is the force of friction? **b.** By putting wheels on the crate, the force of friction is reduced to 2 N. How much force is now needed to push the crate?

7. HYPOTHESIZE: On rainy days, the amount of friction between the road and the wheels of a car can sometimes be reduced by half. Why would reducing friction not be helpful in this case?

DESIGNING AN EXPERIMENT

Design an experiment to solve the following problem. Include a hypothesis, variables, a procedure, and a data table to be completed.

PROBLEM: Which is more effective in reducing friction between a block of steel and a smooth, flat surface, rollers or a lubricant?

Real-Life Science

FRICTION AND SKIING

Friction is one of the major forces that affects the movement of skis across a snow-covered surface. Friction can slow the speed of a downhill racer. That same friction makes it possible for another skier to make sharp turns while maneuvering through a slalom course.

A good ski run can be affected by the type of snow on the course. In some cases, the snow might be icy or crusty. At other times, it may be soft and sticky. Skiers often apply wax to the bottom of their skis in order to adapt to the snow conditions, especially when the snow is soft or wet.

▲ **Figure 1-20** Waxing skis reduces friction and helps to increase speed.

The type of equipment a skier uses is also important. The skis used for cross-country skiing are longer and narrower than those used for downhill skiing.

Thinking Critically What things can a skier do to adapt to varying snow conditions?

1-6 What is air resistance?

INVESTIGATE

Observing Air Resistance
HANDS-ON ACTIVITY

1. Obtain two identical sheets of paper. Crumple one sheet into a ball.
2. Hold the crumpled sheet of paper in one hand and the uncrumpled sheet in the other hand. Extend your arms straight out in front of you at shoulder height.
3. Release both sheets of paper at the same time and observe them fall.

THINK ABOUT IT: Both sheets of paper are identical, yet one fell faster than the other. Why do you think this happened?

STEP 2

Objective
Explain how air resistance affects moving objects.

Key Terms
air resistance: force that opposes the movement of an object in air

terminal velocity: speed at which air resistance and gravity acting on a falling object are equal

vacuum: empty space

Falling Objects The force that opposes the downward motion of objects falling through Earth's atmosphere is called **air resistance.** Air resistance is not the same for all objects. The greater the surface area of an object, the greater the air resistance. Suppose, for example, an oak leaf and an acorn fall from a tree. The leaf flutters slowly to the ground, whereas the acorn drops straight down. As each object falls, air pushes up against the surfaces of the objects. The leaf has a greater surface area than the acorn. As a result, air pushes with more force against the leaf than it does against the acorn. The leaf is slowed more than the acorn, so the acorn hits the ground first.

 PREDICT: Which falling object will hit the ground first, a marble or a feather?

Terminal Velocity When an object is dropped from a high place, gravity pulls the object toward Earth. As it falls, gravity causes the object to accelerate. Its velocity and air resistance increase at steady rates. At some point, the upward force of air resistance becomes equal to the downward pull of gravity. At this point, the object reaches its **terminal velocity.** It stops accelerating and its velocity remains the same for the rest of its downward trip.

2 DESCRIBE: What happens to an object's velocity as it falls?

Free Fall A **vacuum** is empty space. If a bowling ball and a sheet of paper were dropped from the same height in a vacuum, they would hit the ground at the same time. Because there is no air in a vacuum, there is no air resistance to slow the objects as they fall.

▲ **Figure 1-21** When on the Moon's surface, an astronaut dropped a hammer and a feather to test the idea of free fall.

All objects fall at the same speed in a vacuum. When the Apollo astronauts landed on the moon, they tested this idea. There is no air on the moon. One of the astronauts dropped a feather and a hammer at the same time and from the same height. Look at Figure 1-21. What do you think happened? The hammer and the feather hit the ground at the same time!

▶ **DEFINE:** What is a vacuum?

✓ CHECKING CONCEPTS

1. When an object is first dropped, its speed _____.

2. As an object falls, it will reach _____ because of air resistance.

3. When you drop an object, _____ slows it down.

4. There is no _____ in a vacuum.

5. All objects accelerate at the same rate in a _____.

💡 THINKING CRITICALLY

6. **HYPOTHESIZE:** Certain birds spread their wings before they land. Why do they do this? Explain.

Web InfoSearch

Effects of Streamlining A large truck and a sports car traveling at the same speed both have to overcome air resistance. Because of its size and shape, the truck has more air resistance acting on it than does the sports car. The sports car has less surface area. Also, the sports car is streamlined. Its shape has been designed to help reduce air resistance.

SEARCH: Cars, airplanes, and other vehicles all have to overcome air resistance as they move. Use the Internet to find out how engineers design shapes to reduce air resistance. Start your search at www.conceptsandchallenges.com. Some key search words are **streamlining air resistance, wind tunnel streamlining,** and **streamlining airplanes.**

How Do They Know That?

WEIGHT DOESN'T MATTER

All falling objects speed up as they fall. Until Galileo, everyone believed that if two objects of different weight were dropped from some height at the same time, the heavier object would reach the ground first. During a storm, Galileo watched hailstones of different size and weight fall. Based on what he saw, Galileo hypothesized that weight had little or no effect on the change in speed of a falling object.

Legend has it that, to test his idea, Galileo climbed to the top of the Leaning Tower of Pisa. He dropped two rocks of different weight from the tower at the same time. People at the base of the tower saw the two rocks hit the ground at the same time. It is not clear whether or not Galileo actually did this experiment. But he did test and prove his hypothesis.

▲ **Figure 1-22** Galileo may have tested his hypothesis at the leaning tower of Pisa.

Perhaps Galileo's most important contribution to science was his use of the scientific method. Galileo served as a model for all later scientists.

Thinking Critically If a 10-N stone and a 2-N stone are dropped from a tall building at the same time, which will hit the ground first? Explain.

1-7   What is pressure?

Force and Area The amount of force acting on a unit of area is called pressure. **Pressure** is equal to force divided by area. Suppose you hold a can as shown in Figure 1-23. If the can weighs 10 N, it presses down on your hand with a force of 10 N. Now suppose the bottom of the can has an area of 100 cm². The pressure caused by the weight of the can on your hand can be found by using the equation:

$$\text{pressure} = \text{force} \div \text{area}$$
$$\text{pressure} = 10 \text{ N} \div 100 \text{ cm}^2$$
$$\text{pressure} = 0.1 \text{ N/cm}^2$$

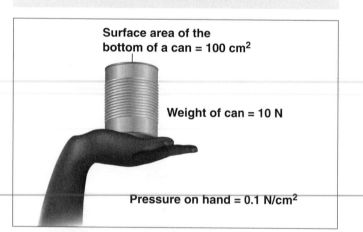

Surface area of the
bottom of a can = 100 cm²

Weight of can = 10 N

Pressure on hand = 0.1 N/cm²

▲ **Figure 1-23** The can exerts pressure on the hand.

1 CALCULATE: How much pressure is produced by a 30-N force acting on an area of 10 m²?

Changing Pressure Pressure can be changed by changing the force. When the area stays the same, increasing the amount of force increases the pressure. Think of a pencil point. Press the point gently against a piece of modeling clay. The point of the pencil will make a small dent in the clay. If you press a little harder, you increase the force and the pressure. The pencil point will sink deeper into the clay.

Pressure can also be changed by changing the area on which the force is pushing. If you apply the same amount of force to a larger area, the pressure is decreased. Think of the same pencil. Turn it around and gently press the eraser against the clay with the same force you used before. The pencil will barely make a mark on the clay. If you increase the force, the eraser will dent the clay but will not sink into the clay as far as the pencil point did. This shows that the pressure applied with the eraser is less than the pressure applied with the point of the pencil.

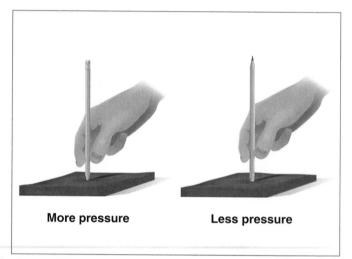

More pressure   Less pressure

▲ **Figure 1-24** The pencil point exerts more pressure than the eraser.

2 LIST: What are two ways to change the amount of pressure being exerted?

Pressure in Nature Pressure can also be found and felt in nature. When pumped into a tire or a balloon, air exerts pressure to keep the item inflated. The air pressure in a tire can be great enough to support the weight of a truck. The pressure exerted by moving air, or wind, can turn the vanes of a windmill or keep a kite flying.

Deep below Earth's surface, pressure is very great. The weight of rocks and soil above can cause dramatic changes in rocks at great depths. Pressures build up to cause volcanoes to erupt and earthquakes to occur.

3 LIST: Name some examples of pressure in nature.

✔ CHECKING CONCEPTS

1. Pressure is equal to force divided by _____ .

2. Pressure can be measured in _____ /cm².

3. You can decrease pressure by _____ the amount of force on the same area.

4. If you increase the area on which a force acts, you will _____ the pressure.

💡 THINKING CRITICALLY

5. CALCULATE: Find the amount of pressure for each of the following examples. **a.** How much pressure is applied when a 50-N force acts over an area of 10 m²? **b.** What will happen to the pressure if the force is increased to 60 N? **c.** How could you decrease the pressure from 6 N/m² to 3 N/m²?

6. ANALYZE: A rectangular building brick rests on a tabletop. How can you change the amount of pressure the brick exerts on the tabletop?

7. ANALYZE: You can get a stronger spray of water from a garden hose if you make the opening of the hose smaller. Explain why.

BUILDING MATH SKILLS

Calculating When you measure, you compare an unknown quantity with a known quantity. You can use the equation pressure = force ÷ area to find the force. To find force, rearrange the equation as follows:

$$\text{force} = \text{pressure} \times \text{area}$$

Use the equation above to find the force for each of the following examples:

8. A pressure of 12 N/m² is applied over an area of 10 m².

9. The contents of a spray can are at a pressure of 1,500 N/mm². The opening of the spray nozzle has an area of 0.2 mm².

10. A pressure of 250 N/cm² is applied to a nail. The point of the nail has an area of 0.25 cm².

⚛ *Hands-On Activity*

OBSERVING AIR PRESSURE

You will need a 2-L plastic bottle with cap, hot water, and cold water.

1. Half-fill a 2-L plastic bottle with hot tap water and screw the cap on tightly.

2. Swirl the hot water around in the bottle for a few seconds.

3. Remove the cap, pour the water out, and quickly replace the cap.

4. Hold the bottle under the cold-water tap for several seconds. Then stand the bottle on a flat surface and observe what happens.

Practicing Your Skills

5. DESCRIBE: What happened to the bottle? What caused this to happen?

6. INFER: What effect did filling the bottle with hot water have?

▲ **STEP 2** Swirl the water in the bottle.

1-8 What is air pressure?

Objective

Explain what causes air pressure and how it is measured.

Key Terms

air pressure: pressure caused by the force exerted by Earth's atmosphere

barometer (buh-RAHM-uht-uhr)**:** instrument used to measure air pressure

Bernoulli's principle: as the speed of a fluid increases, its pressure decreases

Air Pressure Earth's atmosphere is made up of a mixture of gases. This mixture is called air. Air molecules are in constant motion and are pulled toward Earth's center by gravity. The force of all these moving air molecules causes **air pressure.** Most of the air in Earth's atmosphere is concentrated near Earth's surface. So air pressure is greatest near Earth's surface and decreases as altitude increases.

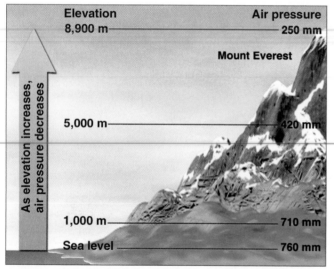

▲ Figure 1-25 Air pressure decreases as altitude increases.

▶ **1** INFER: How does air pressure at the top of a mountain compare with the air pressure at sea level?

Measuring Air Pressure Air pressure is measured with an instrument called a **barometer.** Figure 1-25 shows how a barometer works. The open container and the glass tube contain mercury, a very heavy liquid. The space above the mercury in the tube is a vacuum. As air presses down on the surface of the mercury in the container, the air pressure holds the column of mercury in the glass tube. The greater the air pressure, the higher the mercury will rise in the tube. Normal air pressure at sea level will support a column of mercury 760 mm high in the glass tube. Air pressure decreases with altitude. So, if you carried the barometer up a mountain, the level of the mercury in the tube would move down.

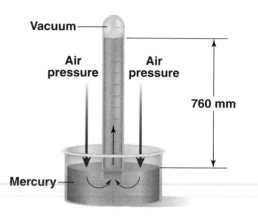

▲ Figure 1-26 A mercury barometer

▶ **2** IDENTIFY: What does a barometer measure?

Bernoulli's Principle Air that is still exerts pressure on Earth's surface. When moving, as in wind, that same air will exert less pressure on the surface. This change in pressure is explained by Bernoulli's principle. **Bernoulli's principle** states that as the speed of a fluid—any gas or liquid—increases, the pressure it exerts decreases. You can try a simple experiment to show this principle. Hold a sheet of paper in front of you. Blow over the top of the paper. The sheet of paper will rise. This shows that the air pressure above the paper has decreased. It is now less than the air pressure beneath the paper, which pushes the paper up.

▶ **3** DEFINE: What is Bernoulli's principle?

Air Pressure and Wing Shape Airplane wings are designed to make use of Bernoulli's principle. Look at the shape of the wing in Figure 1-27. Notice that the top of the wing is more curved than the bottom. As the airplane moves through the air, the shape of the wing causes air pressure on top of the wing to be reduced. So the pressure of the air pushing up on the wing is greater than the pressure of the air pushing down. This unbalanced force, called lift, helps to push the wing up.

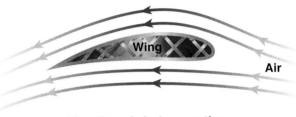

Direction of airplane motion

▲ **Figure 1-27** The shape of an airplane wing helps to create unbalanced forces on the wing.

4 IDENTIFY: What force pushes up on an airplane wing?

Flight Four forces act on an airplane in flight. Figure 1-28 shows a view of an airplane. The arrows show the directions of the four forces.

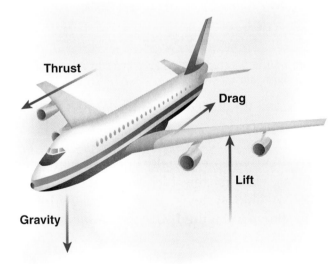

▲ **Figure 1-28** Four forces act on an airplane in flight.

- The weight of the airplane is due to gravity. This force pulls the plane toward the ground.

- The upward force on the bottom of the airplane's wings is called lift. This force pushes the wings up. In normal flight, the lift is equal to the weight of the airplane.

- The forward force on the plane is called thrust. The plane's engines provide the force, or thrust, needed to move the plane forward.

- The flow of air over the wings is a form of air resistance. This frictional force is called drag. Drag slows an airplane down. Too much drag causes the plane to use too much fuel. Engineers design planes that will reduce drag. The process of reducing drag is called streamlining.

5 IDENTIFY: What is the forward force a plane needs in order to fly?

✔ CHECKING CONCEPTS

1. Air pressure is caused by the force of moving _____.

2. A barometer measures _____.

3. Air pressure _____ as altitude increases.

4. As the speed of a fluid increases, the pressure it exerts _____.

5. The force that tends to slow a moving airplane is called _____.

💡 THINKING CRITICALLY

6. HYPOTHESIZE: A plane flying into a strong wind feels more drag than in calm air. Explain.

7. HYPOTHESIZE: When a plane is landing, the flaps under the wings are used to give the plane more drag. Why is this necessary?

Web InfoSearch

Aneroid Barometers Mercury barometers are not always practical to use because they take up so much space. Another type of barometer, called an aneroid barometer, is widely used for its convenience.

SEARCH: Use the Internet to find out how aneroid barometers work and how they can be used to measure altitude. What does *aneroid* mean? Start your search at www.conceptsandchallenges.com. Some key search words are **aneroid barometer, how aneroid barometer works,** and **how barometer works.**

What is water pressure?

Objective

Identify water pressure as the pressure caused by the weight and movement of water molecules.

Water Pressure Like air, water is a fluid. However, water is a liquid. Water molecules are more tightly packed than the molecules that make up air. Water exerts pressure because of the weight and movement of the water molecules. If you place an object in a container of water, the water applies pressure to the object in all directions.

Water pressure changes with depth. There is more pressure on a submarine the deeper it goes underwater. Below certain depths, the pressure from the water is so great that it can crush an object. Submarines are built to withstand a great deal of force from water pressure.

When you dive to the bottom of a swimming pool, you can feel the water pressure, especially against your ears. The pressure of the water is greater than that of the air that normally presses against your body.

▲ **Figure 1-29** How does water pressure at depth *y* compare with that at depth *x*?

1 DESCRIBE: How does water pressure change with depth?

Water Pressure at Home What happens when you open a faucet at home? Hopefully, water comes flowing out in a steady stream. This shows that you have good water pressure in your home. Where does this pressure come from? Some force must be pushing the water out of the faucet.

If your family has its own well, you probably have a system for pumping water up from the well and through the water pipes of your house. The pump provides your water pressure. Chances are your water comes from some central source, such as a town or city water system. In such systems, water is obtained from wells, lakes, or rivers. After being cleaned and purified, the water is pumped into large tanks. The tanks may be on a hill or some location higher than that of the homes they will supply with water. Gravity supplies the force that provides water pressure in such systems.

▲ **Figure 1-30** Gravity provides the force that creates pressure for the water coming from this water tank.

2 EXPLAIN: Why are water tanks located in high places?

Hydraulics Fluids, especially liquids, can transfer pressure. This is the idea behind hydraulic (hy-DRAW-lihk) systems. Look at the hydraulic system shown in Figure 1-31.

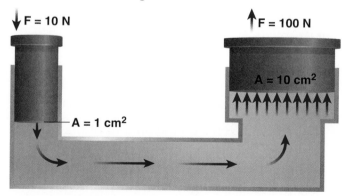

▲ **Figure 1-31** Fluid transfers pressure in this hydraulic system.

This system is filled with a liquid and has two movable pistons. The smaller piston has an area of 1 cm². If you push down on this piston with a force of 10 N, you will apply a pressure of 10 N/cm². This pressure will travel throughout the fluid. When it reaches the larger piston, this pressure will be applied over the entire area of that piston, which is 10 cm². So, a downward force of 10 N on the small piston will produce an upward force of 100 N on the large piston.

3 ▶ DESCRIBE: What happens when pressure is applied to an enclosed fluid?

✓ CHECKING CONCEPTS

1. Water pressure is caused by the weight and _____ of water molecules.

2. Water pressure is _____ than air pressure.

3. _____ provides the force for the water pressure in most homes and offices.

4. Water pressure at a depth of 1 m will be _____ than the pressure at a depth of 5 m.

5. _____ can transfer pressure.

💡 THINKING CRITICALLY

6. **HYPOTHESIZE:** Why does water pressure increase as you move deeper into the water?

HEALTH AND SAFETY TIP

Snorkeling and scuba diving can be educational and great fun. However, these activities can be dangerous. You should always swim and dive with a partner. Don't snorkel or dive in unfamiliar waters. Learn as much as you can about the area you plan to investigate. Be sure to follow all safety precautions. Before diving, take a course and get a dive license.

Hands-On Activity

RELATING PRESSURE AND DEPTH

You will need a milk carton or plastic soda bottle, pencil, paper, metric ruler, modeling clay, basin, apron and safety goggles.

1. Use a pencil to make a hole in a milk carton about 5 cm from the bottom. Plug the hole with modeling clay.

2. Repeat Step 1, making two more holes at distances of 10 cm and 15 cm from the bottom.

3. Put on safety goggles and fill the milk carton with water.

4. Place the carton in a basin or sink and remove the clay plug at the 15-cm hole. Measure and record how far the water squirts.

5. Replug the hole and refill the milk carton with water. Repeat Step 4 for the 10-cm hole and the 5-cm hole.

▲ **STEP 2** Make small holes in the carton.

Practicing Your Skills

6. **DESCRIBE:** From which hole did water squirt the greatest distance? The least distance?

7. **INFER:** From your observations, how does pressure change with depth?

LAB ACTIVITY
Making a Cartesian Diver

Materials

Safety goggles
2-L plastic bottle
  with cap
Plastic pipette
Insulated bell wire
Water
Permanent marker
Metric ruler

BACKGROUND

Pressure affects water and air differently. A plastic bottle filled with air can easily be squeezed with your fingers so that it dents. The pressure applied to the outside of the bottle is transferred to the air inside, squeezing it into a smaller space. However, the same bottle filled with water cannot be squeezed so that it dents. The water inside is not as compressible as air.

What will happen if a bottle that has both air and water inside is squeezed? You can find out by constructing and testing a Cartesian (kahr-TEE-zhuhn) diver.

PURPOSE

In this activity, you will construct a Cartesian diver and experiment with the effects of changing water pressure.

PROCEDURE

1. Copy the chart in Figure 1-32 on a sheet of paper.

2. Use a ruler and marking pen to place marks 5 mm apart on the bulb of the pipette. Then, wrap 10 to 12 coils of insulated bell wire around the pipette. The pipette will be your model diver.

3. Put on safety goggles. Fill a 2-L plastic bottle almost to the top with water.

4. Squeeze the bulb of the pipette and insert the tip into the water. Relax the bulb to draw water into the pipette. Fill the pipette with water.

5. Squeeze the pipette bulb to empty out a small amount of water. Shake it gently to move the air bubble into the bulb.

6. Place the pipette into the bottle and cap it. In your chart, record the level of the water in the pipette.

▲ STEP 2 Prepare the pipette for diving.

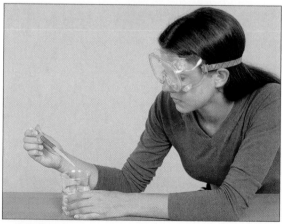

▲ STEP 5 Remove some water from the pipette bulb.

▲ **STEP 7** Squeeze the bottle containing the diver.

▲ **STEP 9** Try to control the depth of the diver.

7. Squeeze the bottle with your hands. If the pipette dives to the bottom, go to Step 8. If the pipette does not dive to the bottom, remove it and squeeze a bit more water out of it. Place it back in the bottle and see if it will dive.

8. Observe and record the water level inside the pipette. Squeeze the bottle to make the diver go to the bottom. Does the water level inside the diver change? If so, how much does it change? Record your observations in the table.

9. Try to make the diver stop halfway to the bottom. Observe and record the water level again.

Comparison of Cartesian Diver Depth with Air Chamber Volume

Depth	Air Chamber Mark	Change (mm)
Surface		
Middle		
Bottom		

▲ **Figure 1-32** Copy this chart and use it to record your observations.

CONCLUSIONS

1. **OBSERVE:** What happened to the Cartesian diver when you squeezed the bottle?

2. **INFER:** What happens to the pressure created by squeezing the bottle?

3. **ANALYZE:** What caused the diver to dive?

4. **HYPOTHESIZE:** Based on your observations, how does a submarine stay underwater?

5. **HYPOTHESIZE:** Why does a diver's ears hurt when he or she descends underwater?

Chapter Summary

Lesson 1-1
- A **force** is a push or a pull.
- A force always acts in a certain direction.
- Weight is a force.

Lesson 1-2
- All objects are attracted to each other because of the force of **gravity** between them.
- The gravitational force between two objects depends on their masses and the distance between them.

Lesson 1-3
- The **newton** (N) is the metric unit of force.
- Weight is a force that is measured in newtons.

Lesson 1-4
- **Friction** is a force that opposes the motion of an object. There are different types of friction.

Lesson 1-5
- Friction can be reduced by changing sliding friction to rolling friction and by using a **lubricant.**

Lesson 1-6
- **Air resistance** is the force that opposes objects moving through air.

Lesson 1-7
- **Pressure** is the amount of force acting on a unit area of a surface.
- Pressure can be changed by changing the amount of force acting on an area or by changing the area on which a force acts.

Lesson 1-8
- **Air pressure** is caused by the weight and movement of air molecules.
- Air pressure is measured with a **barometer.**
- **Bernoulli's principle** says that as the speed of a fluid increases, its pressure decreases.

Lesson 1-9
- Water pressure is caused by the weight and movement of water molecules.
- Water pressure increases with depth.

Key Term Challenges

air pressure (p. 32)
air resistance (p. 28)
balanced forces (p. 16)
barometer (p. 32)
Bernoulli's principle (p. 32)
force (p. 16)
friction (p. 24)
gravity (p. 18)
lubricants (p. 26)
newton (p. 22)
pressure (p. 30)
terminal velocity (p. 28)
unbalanced forces (p. 16)
vacuum (p. 28)

MATCHING **Write the Key Term from above that best matches each description.**

1. metric unit of force
2. substances used to reduce friction
3. empty space
4. force divided by area
5. instrument for measuring air pressure
6. push or pull
7. deals with the pressure of moving fluids
8. force opposing motion
9. maximum velocity for a falling object
10. force of attraction between all objects

FILL IN **Write the Key Term from above that best completes each statement.**

11. When you walk across the floor, there is _____ between your shoes and the floor.
12. As water flows faster through pipes, the pressure on the pipes from the water is decreased. This is an example of _____.
13. When skydivers jump from an airplane, they will reach _____ before landing.
14. Objects fall to the ground because of the force of _____.
15. Earth's force of _____ pulls objects in the direction of Earth's center.
16. The wheels on a skateboard help to reduce _____.

Content Challenges TEST PREP

MULTIPLE CHOICE Write the letter of the term or phrase that best completes each statement.

1. As the wheels of a bicycle move over the surface of the road, they must overcome
   a. sliding friction.
   b. gravity.
   c. rolling friction.
   d. air resistance.

2. An apple falls to the ground because of
   a. a magnetic force.
   b. an electric force.
   c. a gravitational force.
   d. a force of friction.

3. If it takes 25 N to push a car at a constant speed, the friction between the road and the car's tires is
   a. 20 N.
   b. 25 N.
   c. 15 N.
   d. 5 N.

4. A hydraulic lift uses force from
   a. weight.
   b. fluid pressure.
   c. air pressure.
   d. friction.

5. A submarine rising to the surface of the water from deep in the ocean is going from
   a. low pressure to high pressure.
   b. high pressure to low pressure.
   c. zero pressure to high pressure.
   d. high pressure to zero pressure.

6. A ball rolls off a table and hits the floor. The force that caused the ball to hit the floor is
   a. gravity.
   b. friction.
   c. air pressure.
   d. a magnetic force.

7. As an airplane lands, it lowers the flaps under the wings in order to
   a. increase air resistance.
   b. decrease air resistance.
   c. increase the plane's weight.
   d. decrease the plane's weight.

8. A barometer is used to measure
   a. friction.
   b. air pressure.
   c. gravity.
   d. water pressure.

9. An airplane can fly because the pressure on the plane's wings is
   a. greater on the top of the wings.
   b. zero.
   c. greater on the bottom of the wings.
   d. equal on both sides of the wings.

TRUE/FALSE Write *true* if the statement is true. If the statement is false, change the underlined term to make the statement true.

10. Weight is a <u>force</u>.
11. Pressure is equal to force <u>times</u> area.
12. Near Earth's surface, all objects fall in the direction of Earth's <u>center</u>.
13. Air pressure <u>decreases</u> as altitude increases.
14. Moving a box across the floor is an example of <u>rolling</u> friction.
15. A spring scale measures <u>weight</u>.
16. Air resistance <u>slows</u> the speed of a falling object.
17. A lubricant reduces <u>pressure</u>.
18. <u>Friction</u> slows down the motion of objects.
19. The upward force acting on an airplane's wing is called <u>drag</u>.
20. At Earth's surface, a feather falls more slowly than a rock because of <u>air resistance</u>.

Content Challenges TEST PREP

WRITTEN RESPONSE Complete the exercises and answer each of the following questions in complete sentences.

1. DESCRIBE: What effect does altitude have on air pressure? Explain.
2. HYPOTHESIZE: How would the world be different if there were no friction?
3. PREDICT: Will you exert more pressure when you stand on your toes or when you stand flat-footed? Explain.
4. EXPLAIN: Why does an astronaut need to learn about apparent weightlessness?
5. EXPLAIN: Use the principle of hydraulics to explain how some car jacks work.

INTERPRETING A DIAGRAM Use Figure 1-33 to answer the following questions.

6. What force tends to slow the airplane's forward motion?
7. What force opposes the force of gravity?
8. What force is provided by the airplane's engines?
9. Bernoulli's principle helps to explain what force acting on the airplane?
10. What two forces tend to take over when the airplane prepares to land?

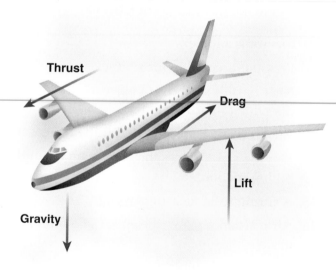

▲ Figure 1-33 Forces acting on an airplane in flight

Chapter 2 Motion

▲ **Figure 2-1** It is the motion of a roller coaster that makes it fun.

A roller coaster can be a lesson in motion. Imagine that everywhere you look, things are moving. Standing on the ground, you see that the roller coaster is moving. If you were in one of the cars, you would feel the motion and see things move past at very fast speeds. Now, suppose you were sitting next to a friend. Throughout the ride, your friend stays beside you. Has your friend moved? Have you?

▶ How can you tell when you or something around you is moving?

Contents

2-1 What are motion and speed?

Objective

Explain that an object is moving if it changes position relative to some object that is not moving.

Key Terms

motion: change in position relative to some fixed object or place

speed: distance traveled per unit of time

average speed: total distance traveled divided by the time it takes to travel that distance

Motion Has anything like this ever happened to you? You see a mail truck parked in front of your house. You run upstairs to get a letter you want to mail. When you come out, the truck is no longer in front of your house. It is now in front of the house next door.

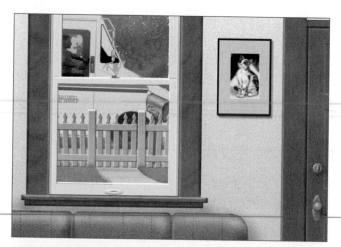

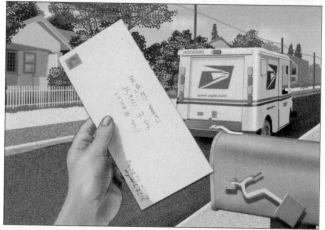

▲ **Figure 2-2** (Top) The position of the mail truck is in front of the house. (Bottom) How do you know the truck has moved?

This example shows that you do not have to see something move to know that motion has taken place. **Motion** is a change in position relative to some fixed object or place. Because you know that your house did not move, the mail truck must have changed position relative to your house.

1 EXPLAIN: How do you tell something has moved?

Motion and Speed When dealing with moving objects, you often want to know how fast something moves. In other words, you want to know how far something travels and how long it takes to make the trip. **Speed** is the distance traveled per unit of time. The SI unit for distance is the meter. Kilometer is often used to measure long distances. The equation for finding speed is shown below.

> speed = distance ÷ time

2 CALCULATE: Which is moving faster, a car traveling 150 km in 3 hours or one traveling 100 km in 2 hours?

Average Speed When traveling in a car, you can tell how fast you are moving at any given instant by looking at the speedometer. This tells your instantaneous speed. You might travel at the same speed for some time. During this time, you would be traveling at a **constant speed**.

▲ **Figure 2-3** An automobile speedometer

However, you seldom travel at the same speed for an entire trip. You probably speed up, slow down, and stop many times. When you finally get to your destination, you can find your average speed for the trip. **Average speed** is the total distance traveled divided by the time it takes to travel that distance.

> average speed = total distance ÷ time

3 CALCULATE: If you traveled 360 km in 4 hours, what was your average speed?

☑ CHECKING CONCEPTS

1. A change in position relative to some fixed object or place is called _____.
2. The equation for calculating speed is _____ divided by time.
3. The speedometer of a car tells you your _____ speed.
4. Speed that does not change is called _____ speed.
5. The total distance traveled divided by the time it takes to travel that distance gives you the _____.

💡 THINKING CRITICALLY

6. **COMPARE:** Explain the difference between instantaneous speed and average speed.
7. **CALCULATE:** If a car travels at an average speed of 90 km/h, how long will it take the car to travel 360 km?
8. **INFER:** A car makes a trip of 400 km in 4 hours. The return trip takes $3\frac{1}{2}$ hours. What can you infer about the average speed of the car on two trips?

BUILDING MATH SKILLS

Analyzing a Graph The distance an object travels in a certain amount of time can be shown on a graph. Figure 2-4 shows distance and time for a car trip. How far does the car travel in 5 hours? What was the average speed of the car during that time? What was the speed of the car between the second and third hours? What was the car's average speed during the first 2 hours? The last 2 hours?

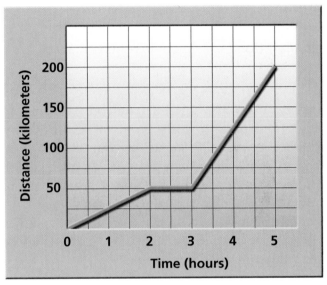

▲ Figure 2-4

Hands-On Activity

MEASURING AVERAGE SPEED

You will need a book, a piece of cardboard, a metric ruler, a watch or clock with a second hand, and a marble.

1. You will need about 1.5 m of floor space. Fold the piece of cardboard lengthwise. Place one end of the cardboard on a book so that the end of the cardboard is raised 1.5 cm off the floor.
2. Hold the marble at the raised end of the cardboard. Release the marble and let it roll down the center of the cardboard and across the floor.
3. Measure the distance in centimeters the marble rolls from the end of the cardboard in 2 seconds. Record your measurement in a table.
4. Repeat Steps 2 and 3 three more times. Record your measurements.

▲ **STEP 2** Allow the marble to roll down the slope.

Practicing Your Skills

5. **OBSERVE:** What was the average distance the marble rolled in 2 seconds?
6. **CALCULATE:** What was the average speed of the marble?

2-2 What are velocity and acceleration?

Objective
Differentiate between speed, velocity, and acceleration.

Key Terms
velocity (vuh-LAHS-uh-tee): speed and direction

acceleration (ak-sehl-uh-RAY-shuhn): rate of change in velocity over time

Speed, Velocity, and Direction When you move from place to place, you travel at different speeds. However, to describe your motion, you need to know more than just your average speed. You must also know the direction in which you are moving. Speed and direction describe **velocity.** An example of velocity is 90 km/h west. Your speed is 90 km/h and your direction is west. Together, these two values describe your velocity.

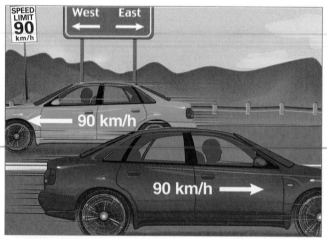

▲ **Figure 2-5** The cars are traveling at the same speed but their velocities are different.

▶1 **INTERPRET:** In Figure 2-5, what is the velocity of the red car? The blue car?

Acceleration When a car changes speed or direction, it is accelerating. **Acceleration** is a change in velocity. When a car speeds up, its velocity is changing. The car is accelerating. When a car slows down, it is also changing velocity. It is

accelerating. When a car goes around a curve or turns a corner, it is changing direction. A change in direction is a change in velocity. The car is accelerating. The initial velocity of the runners in Figure 2-6 is 0. So, as soon as they move down the track, they are accelerating.

◀ **Figure 2-6** From the minute they leave the starting blocks, these runners are accelerating.

▶2 **INFER:** Why is a car accelerating when it turns a corner?

Measuring Acceleration Acceleration describes how fast the velocity of a moving object is changing. To find average acceleration, you must know the change in velocity and the time it takes for the change to occur. The equation for finding acceleration in a straight line is shown here.

> acceleration = change in velocity ÷ time, or
> acceleration = (final velocity − initial velocity) ÷ time

Suppose a car is stopped at a red light. When the light turns green, the car accelerates to a speed of 150 m/sec. The car takes 10 seconds to reach this speed. What is its acceleration?

> acceleration = (150 m/s − 0 m/s) ÷ 10 s
> acceleration = 150 m/s ÷ 10 s
> acceleration = 15 m/s/s

The acceleration is 15 meters per second per second, or 15 m/s². This means that the car's velocity increases 15 m/s every second.

3 ▸ INFER: What is the initial velocity of the car?

☑ CHECKING CONCEPTS

1. What is velocity?
2. What does velocity tell you about a moving object?
3. What is a change in velocity called?
4. What is the formula for finding acceleration?
5. How do you find a change in velocity?

💡 THINKING CRITICALLY

6. COMPARE: A truck is traveling east on a highway at 80 km/h. What is its velocity?
7. ANALYZE: A highway speed limit is 90 km/h. Is this average speed or instantaneous speed? Explain.

BUILDING MATH SKILLS

Interpreting Tables When an object falls through the air, it accelerates as it falls. When it is released, its speed is zero. As it falls, its speed increases. Figure 2-7 shows how the speed of a falling object changes.

ACCELERATION OF A FALLING OBJECT	
Time (seconds)	Velocity (m/sec downward)
0	0
1	9.8
2	19.6
3	29.4
4	39.2
5	0

▲ **Figure 2-7**

What is the object's acceleration from 0 to 1 s? From 0 to 3 s? From 2 s to 4 s? Based on your calculations, what can you say about the acceleration of a falling object?

Hands-On Activity

CHANGING ACCELERATION

You will need a large rubber band, a toy car, a metric ruler, a pencil, and paper.

1. Place the car on the floor. Hold one end of the rubber band on one side of the car while a partner holds the other end.
2. Pull the rubber band and the car a distance of 5 cm, as shown in the picture. Release the rubber band. Measure and record the distance the car travels.
3. Repeat Steps 1 and 2 two more times. The first time pull the rubber band and car back 10 cm. The second time pull them back 15 cm.

▲ **STEP 2** Making the car accelerate

Practicing Your Skills

4. ANALYZE: What supplied the force to make the car accelerate?
5. OBSERVE: How did increasing the force affect the acceleration of the car?

2-3 What is momentum?

Objective

Define and describe how to calculate momentum.

Key Terms

momentum: a property of all moving objects

law of conservation of momentum: total momentum of any isolated system always remains the same

Momentum Picture a bowling ball with a mass of 5 kg rolling toward the pins at the end of the alley. In the next alley, a ball with a mass of 8 kg is rolling toward the pins with the same velocity. Which ball do you think is likely to knock over more pins? If you answered the ball with the greater mass, you are correct. As long as the two bowling balls are moving with the same velocity, the ball with the greater mass will strike the pins with greater energy. The combined effect of the mass and velocity of an object is momentum. **Momentum** is a property of all moving objects.

▲ **Figure 2-8** Momentum is transferred from the ball to the pins.

1▶ IDENTIFY: What two factors determine momentum?

Calculating Momentum The momentum of an object can be found by multiplying its mass by its velocity.

$$\text{momentum} = \text{mass} \times \text{velocity}$$

Let's look at the two bowling balls described earlier. Suppose the velocity of each ball is 20 m/s. Find the momentum of the 5-kg ball.

$$5 \text{ kg} \times 20 \text{ m/s} = 100 \text{ kg-m/s}$$

The 5-kg ball has a momentum of 100 kg-m/s. Now find the momentum of the 8-kg ball.

$$8 \text{ kg} \times 20 \text{ m/s} = 160 \text{ kg-m/s}$$

The 8-kg ball has a momentum of 160 kg-m/s. The ball with more momentum will knock over more pins.

2▶ CALCULATE: Find the momentum of a 10-kg object moving at a velocity of 20 m/s.

Conservation of Momentum When one moving object collides with another object, the motion of both objects changes. For example, when a bowling ball strikes the pins, the bowling ball slows down. It loses momentum. The pins move. The pins gain momentum. The important thing to remember is that the total momentum of the ball and the pins remains the same. In any isolated system, momentum can be transferred but cannot be lost. This is the **law of conservation of momentum.**

Figure 2-9 demonstrates this idea. If a sphere on the left is swung and strikes the row of spheres, a sphere on the other end will move. The momentum of the first sphere is transferred through the row of spheres to the sphere at the other end. No momentum is lost.

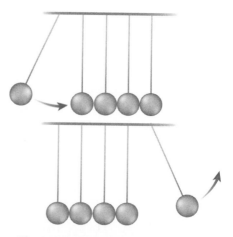

▲ **Figure 2-9** Momentum is conserved as it is transferred from sphere to sphere.

Now suppose two spheres are allowed to strike the remaining row of spheres. Figure 2-10 shows what would happen.

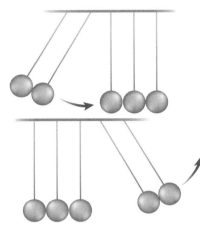

▲ **Figure 2-10** Momentum is still conserved.

3 INFER: What will happen if three spheres are allowed to strike the row of spheres?

✔ CHECKING CONCEPTS

1. The momentum of an object depends on its _____ and its velocity.

2. When a bowling ball strikes the pins, the ball _____ momentum.

3. If the velocity of a car traveling at 50 km/h changes to 30 km/h, the momentum of the car will _____.

4. If several objects are traveling at the same velocity, the object with the greatest mass will have the greatest _____.

💡 THINKING CRITICALLY

5. DESCRIBE: Describe the momentum changes that might occur when a large glass marble rolling across a smooth surface makes a direct hit on a smaller glass marble that is not moving.

6. CALCULATE: Find the momentum of a 25-kg mass moving with a velocity of 25 m/sec.

DESIGNING AN EXPERIMENT

Design an experiment to solve the following problem. Include a hypothesis, variables, a procedure, and a type of data to study.

PROBLEM: How can you show that the momentum of an object is related to its mass?

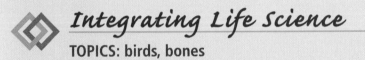

Integrating Life Science

TOPICS: birds, bones

ANIMALS AND MOMENTUM

Most birds can fly. Their hollow bones make for a light body weight. The most difficult parts of a bird's flight are the takeoff and the landing. Both require a change in momentum.

In order to take off, birds have to build up enough speed so that the lift from their wings is greater than their body weight. Small birds can take off with a hop and a flap of their wings. Larger birds, like the flamingos in Figure 2-11, have more of a problem. Because they have more mass, they need more momentum to reach the speed needed to take off. They do this by running as fast as they can while they flap their wings.

▲ **Figure 2-11** Flamingos during takeoff

For some birds, landing is even harder than taking off. Birds cannot just stop flapping their wings. They would drop like a stone. Instead, they twist and spread their wings so that they slow down gradually. In other words, they lose momentum slowly enough to allow them to make a safe landing.

Thinking Critically Why do large birds need more momentum than small birds do in order to take off?

THE Big IDEA

How does safety technology change momentum?

Momentum is a property of all moving objects. An object's momentum can be found by multiplying its mass by its velocity. Many safety devices, such as automobile airbags and protective helmets, are designed to decrease an object's momentum gradually. They do this by changing the velocity—and thus the momentum—of the moving object over as long a time as possible. This is what the mattress does. Physicists use the term *impulse* to describe change in momentum over a given period of time.

Think about how an automobile airbag works. When a person moving at a high speed hits an inflated airbag, the person's momentum is transferred to the particles of air in the bag. The particles speed up. The person loses velocity, and momentum, slowly and safely. If that person were to hit a hard object, such as the dashboard, that person's velocity and momentum would change all at once, perhaps resulting in serious injury.

Protective headgear, such as a bicycle helmet, has some sort of protective lining. When a hard object strikes the helmet, the lining absorbs much of the shock. The object loses momentum slowly, so the effect of its impact on your head is less severe.

Look at the photos and text that appear on these two pages. Then, follow the directions in the Science Log to find out more about "the big idea." ✦

Stuntperson's Fall Cushion
The trick to falling safely from a tall building is to land on something that moves with you when you hit it. The air-filled "pillow" at the base of the building acts like the airbag in a car. It allows the stuntperson to lose momentum slowly and safely.

Space Shuttle Parachute

The parachute increases air resistance. It helps to decrease the momentum of the space shuttle slowly upon landing.

WRITING ACTIVITY

Science Log

Think of some safety devices that protect people in moving vehicles or in sports. Draw a picture of one piece of safety gear. Describe the forces involved and how the device gives protection. Start your search at www.conceptsandchallenges.com.

Highway Crash Barriers

These plastic containers are filled with sand. If a car hits such a container, much of the car's momentum is transferred to the sand. The car loses momentum much more slowly than it would if it ran directly into the concrete.

Car Airbags

Airbags give accident victims more time to slow down than they would have if they crashed into something hard such as a steering wheel.

2-4 What is Newton's first law of motion?

INVESTIGATE

Observing Newton's First Law
HANDS-ON ACTIVITY

STEP 2

1. Lay a board about 2 m long on the floor. Place a toy car at one end of the board.
2. Slowly lift the end of the board with the toy car until the car starts to move. Hold the end of the board at that level. Have a partner measure the height to which the end of the board was raised. Record this measurement.
3. Press a piece of modeling clay on the top of the toy car to increase its mass. Repeat Steps 1 and 2.
4. Predict how adding a second piece of clay to the car will affect the height you will have to raise the board before the car moves. Record your prediction. Repeat Steps 1 and 2 to test your prediction.

THINK ABOUT IT: What keeps the car from moving along the board as it begins to rise? What outside force finally causes the car to move?

Objective
Describe Newton's first law of motion.

Key Term
inertia (ihn-UR-shuh)**:** tendency of an object to stay at rest or in motion

Inertia Place a book on your desk. Does the book move? Unless you push the book, it will remain where you put it without moving. Imagine a spacecraft moving through space. When the engines are turned off, the spacecraft will coast through space at the same speed and in the same direction. The book and the spacecraft have **inertia**. Because of inertia, an object at rest tends to stay at rest. An object in motion tends to keep moving at a constant speed in a straight line.

▶ **IDENTIFY:** What causes a book on a table to remain at rest?

Newton's First Law Newton's first law of motion explains how inertia affects moving and nonmoving objects. Newton's first law states that an object will remain at rest or move at a constant speed in a straight line unless it is acted on by an unbalanced force.

According to Newton's first law, an unbalanced force is needed to move the book on your desk. You could supply the force by pushing the book. An unbalanced force is needed to change the speed or direction of the spacecraft. This force could be supplied by the spacecraft's engines.

▶ **PREDICT:** According to Newton's first law of motion, what will happen to an object at rest if no unbalanced force acts on it?

Effects of Inertia You can see the effects of inertia everywhere. In baseball, for example, to overcome inertia a base runner has to "round" the bases instead of making sharp turns.

◀ **Figure 2-12**
The base runner is fighting to overcome inertia as he rounds the bases.

As a more familiar example of inertia, think about riding in a car. You and the car have inertia. If the car comes to a sudden stop, your body tends to keep moving forward. When the car starts moving again, your body tends to stay at rest. You move forward because the car seat exerts an unbalanced force on your body.

3 EXPLAIN: Why do you keep moving forward when the car in which you are riding stops?

 CHECKING CONCEPTS

1. In space, a spacecraft with its engines turned off will move with constant speed in the same _____.

2. A book will not move by itself because it has _____.

3. A book will remain at rest unless it is acted on by an _____ force.

4. When a car stops suddenly, your body tends to keep moving _____.

5. Newton's first law explains how inertia affects moving and _____ objects.

 **THINKING CRITICALLY**

6. PREDICT: Push a roller skate across a smooth surface. Will the skate keep moving when you stop pushing? Explain.

INTERPRETING VISUALS

Look at Figure 2-13 to answer the following question.

7. In terms of inertia, explain what happens to the coin when the card is flicked away.

▲ Figure 2-13

Real-Life Science

SPORTS AND INERTIA

Inertia plays an important role in most sports. Look at the soccer ball in Figure 2-14. It's just sitting there. Because of inertia, it will stay there until some force causes it to move. As you can see, that force is on the way! Think of the goalkeeper waiting for a ball to be sent speeding toward the goal. If his reflexes are quick enough, he will be able to change the speed or direction of any ball coming his way.

A downhill skier deals with inertia throughout her run. At the top of the mountain, she has to push off to overcome her own inertia. Once she gets moving, inertia will tend to keep her moving down the slope in a straight line. But the course has a lot of curves! So she has to use all of her skill to twist and turn down the course. At the end, she must overcome inertia to bring herself to a safe stop.

Try to think of a sport or game that does not require a person to deal with inertia. Even a checker will stay on a square until someone moves it to another square!

▲ Figure 2-14 The inertia of the soccer ball is about to be changed by an unbalanced force.

Thinking Critically Who would have to overcome more inertia to move the ball, a golfer or a soccer player?

2-5 What is Newton's second law of motion?

Objective
Describe Newton's second law of motion.

Key Term
newton: SI unit of force

Effects of Unbalanced Forces Unbalanced forces cause acceleration. When an unbalanced force acts on an object, the motion of the object is changed. If the object is at rest, the force makes it move. If the object is in motion, the force changes its velocity. Any change in velocity is an acceleration.

 DESCRIBE: What effect does an unbalanced force have on a moving object?

Force, Mass, and Acceleration The amount by which an object accelerates depends on three things. They are the size of the force, the direction in which the force acts, and the mass of the object. Look at Figure 2-15. If two forces act on the same object, the greater force will produce more acceleration than the smaller force.

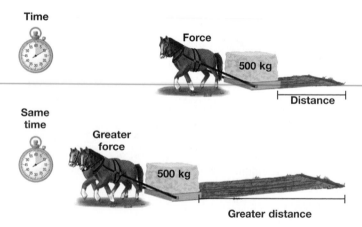

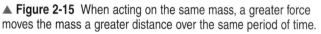

▲ **Figure 2-15** When acting on the same mass, a greater force moves the mass a greater distance over the same period of time.

Now look at Figure 2-16, which shows the same amount of force applied to two objects with different masses. The object with the smaller mass will be accelerated more than the object with the larger mass.

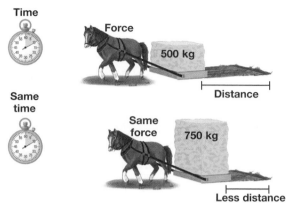

▲ **Figure 2-16** When acting on different masses, the same force will move the smaller mass a greater distance over the same period of time.

IDENTIFY: What three factors affect the acceleration of an object?

Newton's Second Law Newton's second law describes the relationship among force, mass, and acceleration. Newton's second law states that the unbalanced force acting on an object is equal to the mass of the object times its acceleration. Newton's second law can be described by this equation.

$$F = m \times a.$$

In this equation, F is the force, m is the mass, and a is the acceleration. When the mass is measured in kilograms and the acceleration is measured in meters per second per second, the force is measured in newtons (N). A **newton** is the SI unit of force. An unbalanced force of 1 N will accelerate a mass of 1 kg at 1 m/s². One newton of force is equal to one kilogram-meter per second per second (1 kg-m/s²).

DEFINE: What is 1 N of force equal to?

Using Newton's Second Law If no friction is involved, how much force would you have to apply to 10-kg object to make it accelerate at a rate of 45 m/s²? This may seem like a difficult problem at first. However, if you use the equation for Newton's second law, it becomes easy.

$$F = m \times a$$
$$F = 10 \text{ kg} \times 45 \text{ m/s}^2$$
$$F = 450 \text{ kg-m/s}^2$$

You would have to apply a force of 450 kg-m/s², or 450 N.

4 ▶ CALCULATE: How much force is needed to give a 5-kg mass an acceleration of 20 m/s²?

✓ CHECKING CONCEPTS

1. When it is acted on by an unbalanced force, an object will _____.

2. When an unbalanced force acts on an object at rest, the object will _____.

3. A change in velocity is called _____.

4. A large force will cause _____ acceleration than a small force.

5. Newton's second law of motion states that force is equal to _____ times acceleration.

6. The _____ is a unit of force equal to 1 kg-m/s².

💡 THINKING CRITICALLY

Use the equation F = m × a to answer the following questions. Show your calculations.

7. CALCULATE: What force is needed to accelerate a 2-kg mass at rest to a rate of 1 m/s²?

8. With what force would you have to push a 50-kg skater to increase the skater's speed by 2 m/s²?

INTERPRETING VISUALS

Look at Figure 2-17 to answer the question.

9. Will the acceleration of the piano be greater in A or in B? Use Newton's second law of motion to explain your answer.

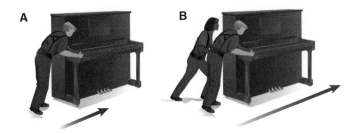

▲ Figure 2-17

People in Science

SIR ISAAC NEWTON (1642–1727)

Isaac Newton was born in England on December 25, 1642. He was a physicist, an astronomer, and a mathematician. At the age of 45, Newton published his theories of motion and gravity. Newton's great book is usually called the *Principia*. It is considered one of the most important works in the history of science.

In the *Principia*, Newton explained his three laws of motion and his theory of gravitation. Newton also invented a branch of mathematics called calculus to help predict motion using his three laws. Newton also made many important discoveries about light and color.

Newton was a professor of mathematics at Cambridge University and a member of the Royal Society. He was knighted by Queen Anne in 1705. Newton once said about himself, "If I have seen further than others, it is because I have stood on the shoulders of giants."

▲ Figure 2-18 Sir Isaac Newton

Thinking Critically What do you think Newton meant by his statement?

What is Newton's third law of motion?

Observing Newton's Third Law
HANDS-ON ACTIVITY

1. Blow up a balloon. Hold the neck of the balloon tightly to prevent air from escaping.

2. Hold the balloon at arm's length and observe which direction the neck of the balloon is facing.

3. Release the balloon and observe what happens.

THINK ABOUT IT: What happened when you released the balloon? What do you think caused this to happen? How was the behavior of the balloon related to the direction in which the neck of the balloon was facing?

STEP 2

Objective

Describe Newton's third law of motion.

Key Terms

action force: force acting in one direction

reaction force: force acting in the opposite direction

Action and Reaction Forces always act in pairs. The two forces act in opposite directions. When you push on an object, the object pushes back with an equal force. When the basketball player in Figure 2-19 shoots the ball, he pushes against it. This is the **action force.**

The ball pushes back against the player with a force of the same size. This **reaction force** will cause the wheelchair to move backwards. Notice that the two forces act on different objects. The action force acts on the ball. The reaction force acts on the player.

▶ **CONTRAST:** How are action and reaction forces different?

Newton's Third Law Newton's third law of motion describes action and reaction forces. The law states that for every action force, there is an equal and opposite reaction force. Imagine hitting a tennis ball. The racket exerts a force on the ball. This is the action force. The ball exerts an equal and opposite force on the racket. This is the reaction force.

▲ **Figure 2-19** When the player exerts a force on the ball, the ball exerts an equal force on him.

◀ **Figure 2-20** The tennis racket is about to exert an action force on the ball.

Newton's third law explains how many sports injuries are caused. The more force you use to hit a tennis ball, the more reaction force your arm receives from the racket. Every time your feet hit the ground when you are running, the ground hits your feet with an equal and opposite force.

▶2 **STATE:** What does Newton's third law of motion state?

Balloons and Rockets Newton's third law explains how balloons and rocket engines work. When the neck of an inflated balloon is released, the stretched rubber material pushes against the air in the balloon. The air rushes out of the neck of the balloon. The action of the air rushing from the balloon pushes against the balloon, moving it in the opposite direction.

When rocket fuel is burned, hot gases are produced. These gases expand rapidly and are forced out of the back of the rocket. This is the action force. The gases exert an equal and opposite force on the rocket itself. This is the reaction force. This force pushes the rocket upward.

▲ **Figure 2-21** Action and reaction forces during liftoff

▶3 **INFER:** What effect would blowing more air into a balloon have on the motion of the balloon when released?

✓ CHECKING CONCEPTS

1. Forces always act in _____.
2. A table exerts an upward _____ on objects resting on the table.
3. For every action force, there is an equal and _____ reaction force.
4. In a rocket engine, the _____ force pushes the rocket upward.
5. Action forces and reaction forces always act on _____ objects.

💡 THINKING CRITICALLY

6. **INFER:** An object resting on a table weighs 100 N. With what force is the object pushing on the table? With what force is the table pushing on the object?
7. **CLASSIFY:** When you walk, your feet push against the ground. At the same time, the ground pushes against your feet. Which is the action force? Which is the reaction force?
8. **HYPOTHESIZE:** When you walk, you move forward. Does Earth move in the opposite direction? Explain your answer.

Web InfoSearch

VentureStar In 1996, NASA started plans to develop a replacement for the space shuttle. This replacement, called VentureStar, was to have many improvements over the present shuttle. At present, this project has been postponed. It may be revived in the future.

SEARCH: Use the Internet to find out what types of improvements NASA plans to incorporate in its next generation of space shuttles. What is the X-33? Why does NASA call the VentureStar a Reusable Launch Vehicle? Start your search at www.conceptsandchallenges.com. Some key search words are **X-33, Reusable Launch Vehicle, VentureStar,** and **Lockheed Martin VentureStar.**

LAB ACTIVITY
Investigating Newton's Second and Third Laws

Materials

Newton cart
Safety goggles
Plastic drinking straws
3 rubber bands
Film canister
Sand
Meter stick
String
Scissors

▲ **STEP 3** Use drinking straws to make a track.

▲ **STEP 4** Attach a string loop and rubber band to the Newton cart.

BACKGROUND

Newton's second law describes how force, mass, and acceleration are related. The ability of a rocket to take off from Earth's surface and climb into space depends on the generation of enough force. Newton's third law deals with the action-reaction forces at work when a rocket engine lifts the rocket and pushes it into space. Together, these two laws explain how a rocket is launched into space.

PURPOSE

In this activity, you will experiment with the relationship of mass, acceleration, and force.

PROCEDURE

1. On a separate sheet of paper, make a chart like the one shown in Figure 2-22.

2. Cut three 15-cm pieces of string. Tie the ends of each piece of string to form three loops. Make each loop the same size.

3. On a flat surface, make a track of 20 plastic drinking straws. Lay the straws parallel to each other 4 cm apart.

4. Slip a rubber band through one of the string loops. Slide the rubber band over the two end posts of a Newton cart. Stretch the rubber band until you can slide the string loop over the third post of the cart.

5. Fill a film canister with sand. Place the canister snugly inside the stretched rubber band on the cart.

6. Set the Newton cart on the straws near one end of the track. Point the end of the cart with the single post down the track.

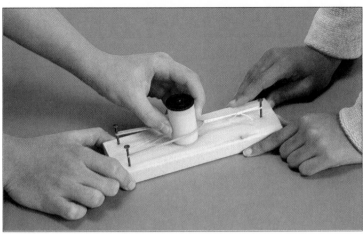

▲ **STEP 5** Place the canister on the Newton cart.

7. Put on safety goggles. Then, carefully cut the string and quickly pull the scissors out of the way. Measure and record the distances that the cart travels.

8. Repeat the activity using two rubber bands and again using three rubber bands. Each additional rubber band increases the force.

▲ **STEP 7** Launch the Newton cart down the track of straws.

Comparison of Acceleration and Distance for the Newton Cart		
Trial	Number of Rubber Bands	Distance Cart Traveled
1		
2		
3		

▲ **Figure 2-22** Copy this chart and use it to record your observations.

CONCLUSIONS

1. **OBSERVE:** What happened to the cart when you cut the string? What happened to the canister?

2. **ANALYZE:** What supplies the action force in this activity?

3. **ANALYZE:** What is the relationship between the amount of force applied and the distance the cart moved?

Chapter 2 Challenges

Chapter Summary

Lesson 2-1
- **Motion** is a change in position.
- **Average speed** is equal to the total distance traveled divided by the total time for the trip.

Lesson 2-2
- **Velocity** describes the speed and direction of a moving object.
- An object is accelerating when there is change in its velocity.
- To find **acceleration,** you must know the change in velocity and the time for the change to occur.

Lesson 2-3
- **Momentum** is a property of all moving objects.
- The momentum of an object is equal to its mass times its velocity.
- The **law of conservation of momentum** states that momentum may be transferred but cannot be lost.

Lesson 2-4
- **Inertia** is the tendency of an object to remain at rest or in motion.
- Newton's first law of motion states that an object will remain at rest or move at a constant speed in a straight line unless it is acted on by an unbalanced force.
- The effects of inertia can be felt every day.

Lesson 2-5
- Unbalanced forces cause objects to accelerate.
- The acceleration of an object depends on the mass of the object and the size and direction of the force acting on it.
- Newton's second law of motion describes the relationship among force, mass, and acceleration ($F = m \times a$).

Lesson 2-6
- Forces always act in pairs.
- Newton's third law of motion states that for every **action force,** there is an equal and opposite **reaction force.**
- Newton's third law explains how rocket engines work.

Key Term Challenges

acceleration (p. 44)
action force (p. 54)
average speed (p. 42)
inertia (p. 50)
law of conservation of momentum (p. 46)
momentum (p. 46)
motion (p. 42)
newton (p. 52)
reaction force (p. 54)
speed (p. 42)
velocity (p. 44)

MATCHING Write the Key Term from above that best matches each description.

1. speed and direction
2. change in velocity
3. mass $\times$ velocity
4. unit of force
5. change in position
6. tendency to remain at rest
7. distance traveled per unit of time

FILL IN Write the Key Term from above that best completes each statement.

8. An object's _____ does not include direction.
9. A property of all moving objects is _____.
10. The rush of gases from a rocket engine provides the _____.
11. Newton's first law deals with _____.
12. A change in position indicates that _____ has taken place.

Content Challenges TEST PREP

MULTIPLE CHOICE Write the letter of the term or phrase that best completes each statement.

1. When you move from place to place, you are changing your
   a. mass.
   b. inertia.
   c. position.
   d. speed.

2. An unbalanced force causes a moving object to change
   a. speed.
   b. direction.
   c. neither speed nor direction.
   d. either speed or direction.

3. A car's speedometer tells you
   a. average speed.
   b. instantaneous speed.
   c. acceleration.
   d. velocity.

4. Balanced forces are always opposite in
   a. direction.
   b. size.
   c. size and direction.
   d. size or direction.

5. Velocity includes speed and
   a. acceleration.
   b. inertia.
   c. direction.
   d. force.

6. Average speed is equal to total distance divided by
   a. average distance.
   b. average time.
   c. instantaneous speed.
   d. total time.

7. Action forces and reaction forces are described by Newton's
   a. first law of motion.
   b. second law of motion.
   c. third law of motion.
   d. law of gravitation.

8. According to Newton's second law of motion, force is equal to mass times
   a. acceleration.
   b. speed.
   c. velocity.
   d. inertia.

9. The newton is a unit of
   a. speed.
   b. force.
   c. velocity.
   d. acceleration.

10. Inertia is described by Newton's
    a. first law of motion.
    b. second law of motion.
    c. third law of motion.
    d. law of gravitation.

TRUE/FALSE Write *true* if the statement is true. If the statement is false, change the underlined term to make the statement true.

11. Speed is distance traveled in a given <u>direction</u>.

12. <u>Velocity</u> is found by multiplying mass by velocity.

13. <u>Momentum</u> can be transferred but cannot be lost.

14. Newton's <u>third</u> law of motion deals with inertia.

15. <u>Unbalanced</u> forces always result in motion.

Concept Challenges TEST PREP

WRITTEN RESPONSE **Complete the exercises and answer each of the following questions in complete sentences.**

1. CONTRAST: What is the difference between average speed and instantaneous speed?

2. HYPOTHESIZE: When does an object have zero acceleration? Explain.

3. EXPLAIN: Two cars are stopped at a red light. When the light turns green, both cars accelerate to a speed of 150 m/s. The first car takes 10 seconds to reach this speed. The second car takes 20 seconds. Which car has the greater acceleration?

4. ANALYZE: An unbalanced force acts on a moving object. The object slows down. In what direction is the unbalanced force acting? How do you know?

INTERPRETING A DIAGRAM **Use Figure 2-23 to answer the following questions.**

5. Does this diagram illustrate speed or velocity? Explain.

6. In what direction is the blue car traveling?

7. In what direction is the red car traveling?

8. What speed limit is shown in the diagram? Is this an average speed or an instantaneous speed?

9. If each car continues moving at an average speed of 90 km/h for 2 hours, how far will each car travel?

10. How much distance will separate the cars after 2 hours?

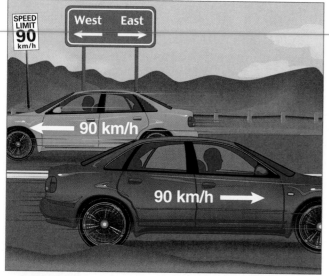

▲ Figure 2-23

Chapter 3 Energy and Work

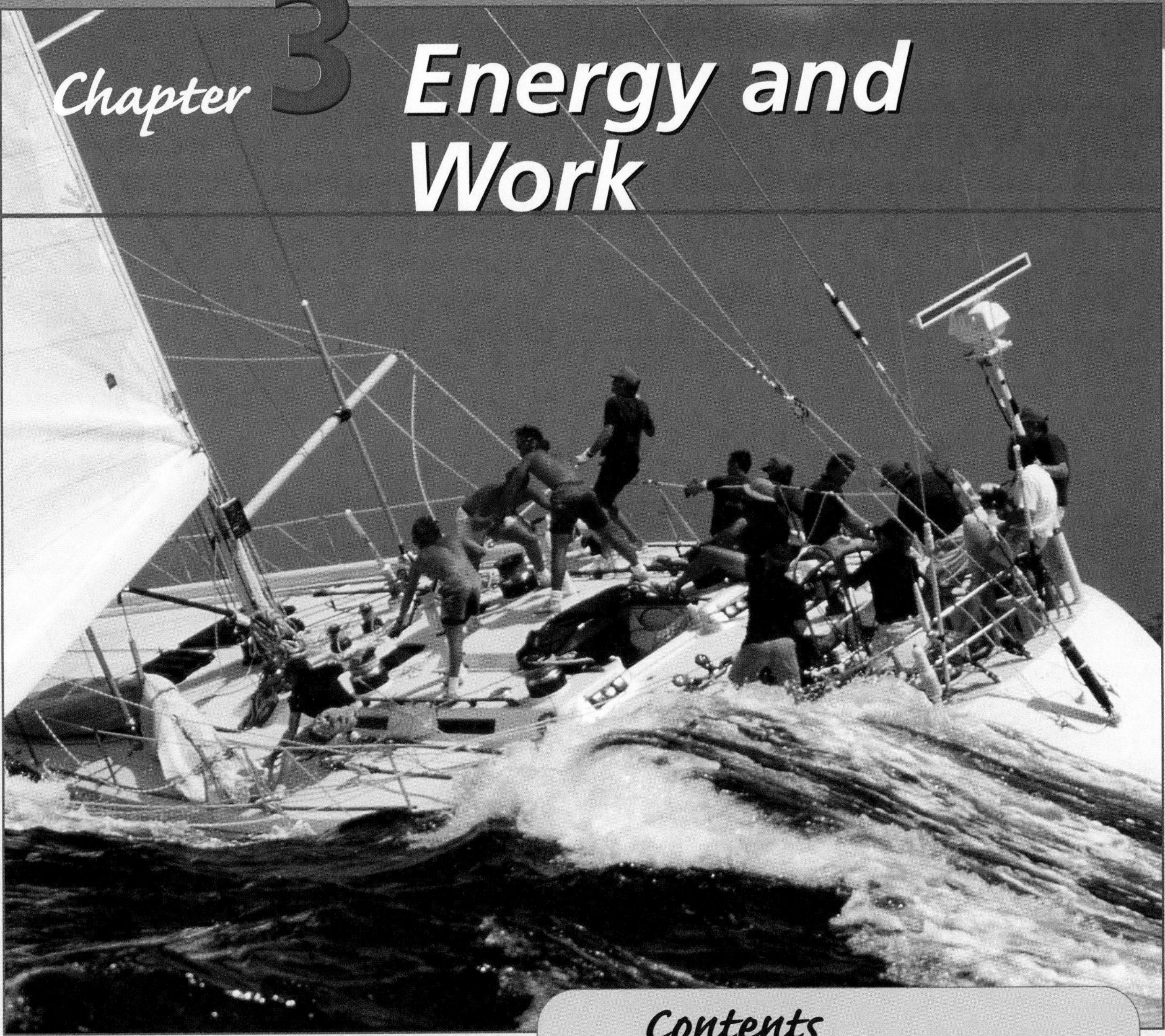

▲ **Figure 3-1** A sailboat race is hard work for everyone.

Contents

Say the word "sailing" and most people will think about a relaxed afternoon on the water. However, racing sailboats is a different story. This sport involves energy and work. From the minute the boat crosses the starting line until it crosses the finish line, nobody relaxes. The work involves turning cranks and pulling lines, raising and lowering sails. Crew members rush back and forth, straining to get every bit of speed possible from the boat.

▶ What outside force helps to move the sailboat?

3-1 What is energy?

Objective
Compare potential energy and kinetic energy.

Key Terms
energy: ability to make something happen

potential (poh-TEHN-shuhl) **energy:** stored energy

kinetic (kih-NEHT-ihk) **energy:** energy of motion

Energy Look at the picture of the dam in Figure 3-2. If you have ever taken a shower or stood out in the rain, you know that falling water has energy. The energy of the water falling through the spillways of a dam can be used to generate electricity. However, did you know that the quiet water in the lake behind the dam also has energy?

Energy is the ability to make something happen. There are two general kinds of energy. These are potential energy and kinetic energy.

▶1 DEFINE: What is energy?

Potential Energy **Potential energy** is stored energy. The energy of the water in the lake behind the dam in Figure 3-2 is potential energy. The water has energy because of its position. Gravity can cause it to fall to the river below the dam. This kind of stored energy is called **gravitational potential energy**.

The gravitational potential energy stored in a sample of matter depends on two factors. These factors are weight and height. The more weight an object has, the more potential energy it has. Potential energy also depends on height. The farther an object has to fall, the more potential energy it has.

The fireworks in Figure 3-3 have a different kind of potential energy called **chemical potential energy**. This potential energy is stored in the chemicals in the fireworks. When the fireworks are set off, the potential energy stored in the chemicals is released as heat, light, and sound.

▲ **Figure 3-3** Fireworks have chemical potential energy.

▶2 IDENTIFY: What kind of energy is released when you strike a match?

Kinetic Energy **Kinetic energy** is energy of motion. Anything that is moving has kinetic energy. When you walk or run, you have kinetic energy. Like potential energy, kinetic energy also depends on two factors. With kinetic energy, the factors are mass and velocity. The faster you move, the more kinetic energy you have. The more mass a moving object has, the more kinetic energy it has.

Think about a car and a truck moving at 30 mph. The truck has the greater mass. So, even though both vehicles are traveling at the same speed, the truck will have more kinetic energy than the car.

▲ **Figure 3-2** The water above this dam has gravitational potential energy.

◀ **Figure 3-4** Both runners are moving at the same speed. Because the runner on the left has more mass, he also has more kinetic energy than the runner on the right.

3 ▶ LIST: What two factors determine how much kinetic energy a moving object has?

✓ CHECKING CONCEPTS

1. The ability to make something happen is _____.
2. Two kinds of energy are potential energy and _____ energy.
3. Stored energy is _____ energy.
4. Kinetic energy is energy of _____.
5. A diver on a diving board has _____ potential energy.

💡 THINKING CRITICALLY

6. COMPARE: What is the difference between potential energy and kinetic energy?
7. ANALYZE: A rock on the edge of a cliff has what kind of energy? When could the rock have both kinetic and potential energy? Explain.

BUILDING MATH SKILLS

If you know the weight of an object and know how high it is above the ground, you can use the formula shown here to find its gravitational potential energy (*PE*).

$$PE = weight \times height$$

Remember that weight is a measure of the pull of gravity on a mass. Weight is measured in newtons (N). Height is measured in meters (m). Therefore, potential energy is expressed in units called newton-meters, or N-m. Use the formula to find the gravitational potential energy of each of the following objects.

• a 50-N brick on top of a 4-m ladder
• a 780-N diver standing on a diving board 10 m above the water

---

◈ *Integrating Earth Science*

TOPIC: erosion

SCULPTING EARTH'S SURFACE

Forces can produce change. Over time, forces such as wind, moving water, and ice change the appearance of Earth's surface. The wearing away of Earth's surface in one place and building it up in another place is called erosion.

Moving water can pick up and carry sediments such as soil and gravel. When it is moving fast enough, water can even roll large rocks along the bed of a river. When these materials drag and bounce along a streambed, they carve new channels. Over millions of years, the Grand Canyon in Arizona was carved out by materials carried in the waters of the Colorado River.

Ocean waves carve the shoreline. They wear away rocks, making cliffs and terraces. Sediments carried by the water scrape against rocky shorelines. Sometimes this carves out caves and arches. Wind and moving ice, called glaciers, are other agents of erosion.

Thinking Critically What part does kinetic energy play in sculpting Earth's surface?

▲ **Figure 3-5** These canyons were carved by the moving water of a river.

3-2 What are different forms of energy?

Objectives
Identify and describe the different forms of energy.

Forms of Energy Your body gets energy from the food you eat. An automobile uses the energy in gasoline to make it move. A clock spring stores energy to turn the hands of the clock. These are some examples of different forms of energy. There are six main forms of energy. They are mechanical energy, electrical energy, electromagnetic energy, heat energy, chemical energy, and nuclear energy.

1 **LIST:** What are six main forms of energy?

Using Forms of Energy You use the different forms of energy without ever noticing them. If energy came only in one form, the campers in Figure 3-6 might have light to see by but no heat for cooking. Each form of energy has its own characteristics and uses.

Mechanical Energy The energy in moving things is mechanical energy. This type of energy can occur as potential or kinetic energy, or both. For example, when you wind the spring on a toy car, you are storing mechanical energy in the spring. When the toy is turned on, the spring unwinds and the mechanical energy of the spring is seen as the toy car moves. Until the spring winds down completely, it has both potential and kinetic energy.

Electrical Energy The energy that flows through wires and powers the lights and appliances in your house is electrical energy. This energy is in the form of moving electric charges.

Electromagnetic Energy Electromagnetic energy is a form of energy that can travel through a vacuum. Visible light, also called radiant energy, is the most familiar form of electromagnetic energy. Other forms of this energy include X-rays, radio waves, and microwaves.

Heat Energy If you rub your hands together, they become warm. Heat energy, also called thermal energy, is the energy of the moving particles that make up matter. The faster the particles move, the more heat energy they have. All forms of matter contain some heat energy.

Chemical Energy The energy that holds particles of matter together is chemical energy. The energy stored in the head of a match is chemical energy. The energy stored in food and in fuels such as wood and coal is chemical energy.

▲ **Figure 3-6** Several forms of energy can be seen at this campsite.

Nuclear Energy Nuclear energy is the energy stored in the nucleus of an atom. Normally this energy is used to keep the protons and neutrons tightly bound together in the nucleus. However, when the nucleus of a large atom is split, as in a nuclear reactor, some of that energy is released as heat and light. Nuclear energy can also be released when nuclei of light atoms combine. The heat and light from the Sun are produced from this type of nuclear reaction.

2 **COMPARE:** Choose two forms of energy. How are they alike? How are they different?

✓ CHECKING CONCEPTS

1. Where does your body get energy from?
2. How many main forms of energy are there?
3. What is mechanical energy?
4. What is the most familiar form of electromagnetic energy?
5. What kind of energy is stored in wood?
6. What is nuclear energy?

💡 THINKING CRITICALLY

7. **CLASSIFY:** Of the six main forms of energy, which forms are potential energy? Which are kinetic energy? Explain your answers.
8. **ANALYZE:** Identify each of the following objects as a source of mechanical, electromagnetic, heat, chemical, or nuclear energy. Some of the objects may be sources of more than one form of energy. Explain your answers.

   a. gasoline   d. river
   b. dynamite explosion   e. lightning
   c. burning wood   f. the Sun

DESIGNING AN EXPERIMENT

Design an experiment to solve the following problem. Include a hypothesis, variables, a procedure, and a type of data to study.

PROBLEM: How can you show that sound is a form of mechanical energy?

Science and Technology

ENERGY IN MEDICINE

Throughout history, medicine has benefited greatly from advances in technology. Much of this technology uses energy. One of the most familiar medical devices is the X-ray machine. X-rays are forms of electromagnetic energy. Like light, X-rays can produce photographs, not of scenery but of bones inside the human body.

Computerized axial tomography is the tongue-twisting name for an advanced X-ray machine known as a CAT scanner. This device includes an X-ray tube. It rotates around a patient producing a three-dimensional image of the internal parts of the body on a computer screen.

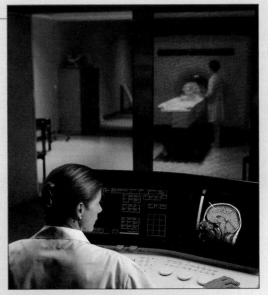
▲ **Figure 3-7** An MRI machine uses magnetic energy.

Magnetic energy and sound energy are also used in medicine. Magnetic resonance imaging (MRI) machines use magnetic energy to study soft tissues of the body. Ultrasound devices use the energy of sound waves to monitor the health of a developing fetus.

Thinking Critically Explain why energy is important to medical science.

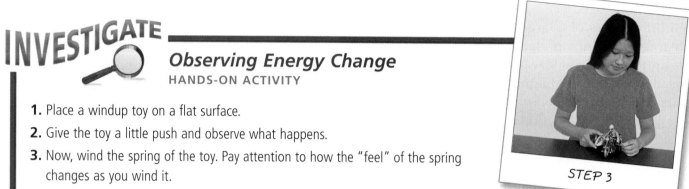

INVESTIGATE

Observing Energy Change
HANDS-ON ACTIVITY

1. Place a windup toy on a flat surface.

2. Give the toy a little push and observe what happens.

3. Now, wind the spring of the toy. Pay attention to how the "feel" of the spring changes as you wind it.

4. Place the toy on a flat surface and release the spring.

THINK ABOUT IT: What kind of energy did the spring have after you wound it? How did this energy change?

STEP 3

Objective
Identify examples of energy changing form.

Key Terms
thermal (THUR-muhl) **pollution:** damage that occurs when waste heat enters the environment

law of conservation of energy: energy cannot be made or destroyed, but only changed in form

Changing Potential and Kinetic Energy

Energy can change from one form to another. Potential energy and kinetic energy often change form. Look at the bouncing ball in Figure 3-8. As the ball falls, potential energy is changed into kinetic energy and back into potential energy as it bounces to a higher position.

The ball in Figure 3-8 has the greatest amount of potential energy at its highest point. It has the greatest amount of kinetic energy just before it hits the ground.

1 ▶ **ANALYZE:** When does a bouncing ball have the least amount of kinetic energy?

Changing Forms of Energy You can observe many examples of changing forms of energy all around you. When you turn on an electric light, electrical energy is changed into light energy and heat energy. When you start an automobile, the engine changes the chemical energy in gasoline into mechanical energy. Nuclear reactors change nuclear energy into heat that is used to generate steam. Your muscles change the chemical energy in food into mechanical energy.

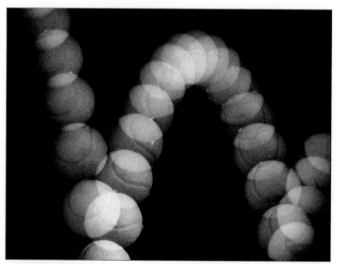

▲ **Figure 3-8** The energy of the bouncing ball is always changing form.

▲ **Figure 3-9** The light energy from the bulb is captured by the solar cells on the calculator. It is changed to electrical energy that powers the calculator.

2 ▶ **IDENTIFY:** What energy change takes place when you turn on an electric light?

Waste Heat When energy changes form, some of the energy is always changed into heat. Most of this heat energy is wasted. When waste heat energy escapes into the environment, it causes **thermal pollution.** For example, the water in lakes and rivers is used to remove waste heat from power plants. The waste heat makes the water warmer. The water may become too warm for living things. If the water gets too warm, fish in the lakes and rivers may die.

▶ **DEFINE:** What is thermal pollution?

Conservation of Energy You know that energy can change from one form to another. Energy can also move from place to place. However, energy can never be lost. Energy can never be created or destroyed. Energy can only be changed in form. This is the **law of conservation of energy.**

Before 1905, the law of conservation of energy did not seem to apply to nuclear energy. In the Sun, nuclear energy is changed into heat energy and light energy. The sun seemed to be producing too much energy for its mass. In 1905, Albert Einstein showed that matter and energy are two forms of the same thing.

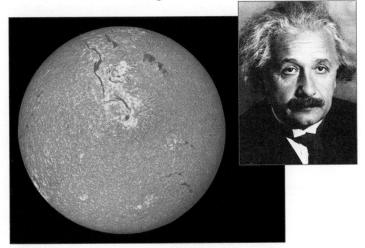

▲ **Figure 3-10** The Sun's energy gave Einstein (inset) the inspiration for his theory about matter and energy.

Einstein concluded that matter can be changed into energy, and energy can be changed into matter. The total amount of matter and energy in the universe does not change. Einstein stated this idea in the following equation.

$$E = mc^2$$

In this equation, E is energy, m is matter, or mass, and c is the speed of light. Einstein's equation showed that a small amount of matter could be changed into a huge amount of energy. This is what happens in the Sun.

▶ **DEFINE:** What is the law of conservation of energy?

CHECKING CONCEPTS

1. A bouncing ball has the greatest amount of _____ energy at the top of its bounce.

2. When a bouncing ball is at the _____ of its bounce, it has the greatest amount of kinetic energy.

3. When you turn on a light, electrical energy is changed into light and _____.

4. An automobile engine changes _____ energy into mechanical energy.

5. The _____ energy in food is changed into mechanical energy by your muscles.

6. A nuclear reactor changes nuclear energy into _____ energy.

THINKING CRITICALLY

7. **SYNTHESIZE:** Think of a thunderstorm. Describe the forms of energy that occur and the effects they have. Explain each time energy changes from one form to another.

INTERPRETING VISUALS

Study the drawings in Figure 3-11 and answer the following questions.

8. What two forms of energy make item A function?

9. How many forms of energy are shown in B? What are they?

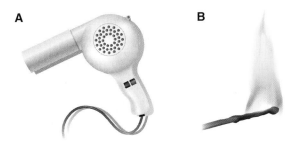

A   B

▲ **Figure 3-11**

THE Big IDEA

What are alternative sources of energy?

Think of the many ways people use energy every day. We use energy to heat and light our homes. Think of the hundreds of different ways we use electricity. Energy is also needed to run all forms of transportation.

Most of the energy people use today comes from burning fossil fuels—oil, coal, and natural gas. However, there are problems with this. Burning fossil fuels creates pollution and increases the greenhouse effect. Also, fossil fuels are not renewable. Once you burn a liter of fuel oil, it is gone forever. So someday, Earth's supply of fossil fuels will run out. It is time to develop some alternative sources of energy.

The Sun is a great energy source. Solar energy is free, and it will be available for billions of years. Drying clothes on a clothesline and using rooftop water heaters are simple ways to use solar energy. Solar panels can capture solar energy and convert it to heat, which can be used to heat our homes.

Wind is another form of "free" energy. This energy source has been used for thousands of years to sail ships, pump water, and grind grain in windmills. Wind can also be used to generate electricity.

The moving water in rivers and tidal basins and heat from below Earth's surface are other natural energy sources. In the future, each of these alternative energy sources may be developed to help replace the energy being produced from fossil fuels today. Look at the pictures on these pages. Then, follow the instructions in the Science Log to find out more about "the big idea."✦

Geothermal Power Generator

In places with lots of volcanic activity, heat energy inside Earth can be tapped to make electricity or heat buildings. Iceland plans to use geothermal and other energy sources to be free of fossil fuels by 2030.

Wind Farm

The energy of the wind can be used to spin an electric generator. In windy places, this is a great renewable energy source.

Energy From Water

For hundreds of years, moving water has turned water wheels to grind grain. Today, moving water is used in hydroelectric plants (above right) to generate electricity.

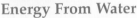

Solar-Powered Highway Emergency Phone

Some emergency phones on the highway are powered with photoelectric cells. In the daytime the sun charges a battery so the phone can work at night.

SPEED LIMIT 15

WRITING ACTIVITY

Science Log:

What alternative energy sources are available where you live? Find out about local renewable energy sources. Think about all the ways you use electricity and other forms of energy in your home. Then, design a house that uses renewable alternatives to fossil fuels to make its energy. Start your search at www.conceptsandchallenges.com.

3-4 What is work?

Objective
Relate work, force, and distance.

Key Term
work: force exerted through a distance

Work When are you doing work? **Work** is done when a force moves an object a certain distance. This relationship can be shown in the following equation.

$$work = force \times distance$$

Suppose two boys push a car stuck in the mud. No matter how hard they push, they are not able to move the car. They are very tired afterward. Did the boys do any work?

The answer is no. For work to be done, something must be moved. The boys used a great deal of energy, but the car did not move. Work was not done.

 DESCRIBE: What is the relationship between work, force, and distance?

Work and Energy Energy has been defined as the ability to make something happen. Energy is also often defined as the ability to do work. When a force moves an object, work is done.

Anything that can make something else move has energy. A moving bowling ball has energy. When the ball hits the pins, the pins move. The energy stored in gasoline can do work. It can make a car move. However, energy can be changed in form without any work being done. If you hold a heavy bag of groceries, your arms will get tired. Chemical energy in your muscles is changed to other forms of energy. However, because this energy is not being used to move the bag of groceries, you are not doing work.

2 **EXPLAIN:** How do you know a moving bowling ball has energy?

Direction of Motion For work to be done, a force must make an object move in the same direction as the force. Look at the three pictures in Figure 3-12. In the first picture, the girl is picking up a backpack. The backpack is moving in the direction of the force she used on it. She is doing work. In the middle picture, she is standing still with the pack on her back. She is using force, but no work is being done. In the third picture, she is moving the backpack as she begins to walk. Because she is causing the backpack to accelerate, she is doing work again.

3 **EXPLAIN:** Why is work done when you lift an object from the floor?

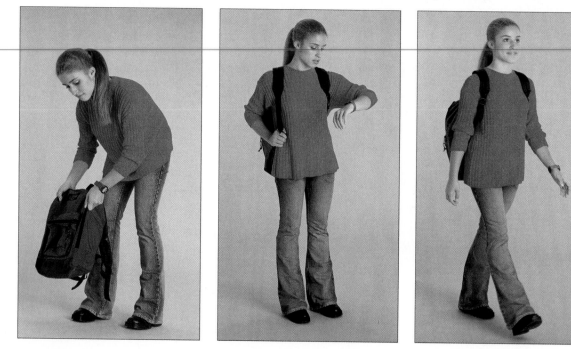

◀ Figure 3-12
Work is being done in the first and last pictures but not the middle picture.

Natural Forces at Work Nature supplies the energy to do all kinds of work. Wind pushes sailboats across water and helps kites to fly. Wind energy turns windmills, which in turn generate electricity. The moving water of a river carries barges and pleasure boats. In the past, moving water turned water wheels that ran machinery in factories. Hurricanes, tornadoes, floods, and earthquakes provide the most dramatic examples of nature's ability to do work.

4 HYPOTHESIZE: What role does gravity play as a natural force doing work?

✔ CHECKING CONCEPTS

1. Work = force × _____.
2. Work is not done unless something is _____.
3. The ability to do work is _____.
4. For work to be done, the direction of the _____ must be the same as the direction of motion.

5. The stored _____ in gasoline can make a car move.

💡 THINKING CRITICALLY

6. ANALYZE: Is work being done in each of the following examples? Explain your answers.
   a. Someone holds a heavy package for one hour.
   b. A football player kicks a field goal.
   c. A tennis player hits a tennis ball over the net.

HEALTH AND SAFETY TIP

Always be careful when picking up any heavy object from the floor. You should bend your knees and use your leg muscles, not your back muscles, to lift the object. Use library references to find out other ways to prevent back injuries.

Real-Life Science

SPORTS AND WORK

Athletes pride themselves on their ability to do work. Most sports involve forces that produce movement. Kicking a football is an example. The force applied to the ball causes it to move downfield in the direction of the force. A field-hockey ball is sent on its way when struck by a hockey stick. A push against a basketball sends the ball in the direction of the basket.

Perhaps the most obvious work done in sports is carried out by weight lifters. The goal of weight lifters is to move heavy objects. Some events involve lifting a heavy barbell from the floor and raising it vertically above the head. Then, the barbell has to be slowly lowered back to the floor. The lowering of the barbell requires a great deal of energy, with the muscles acting against the force of gravity.

▲ **Figure 3-13** Work is done when the barbell is lifted.

Thinking Critically Does the losing team in a tug-of-war contest do any useful work? Explain.

Objective

Use the proper units to measure and express work.

Key Term

joule (JOOL): SI unit of work; equal to 1 N-m (newton-meter)

Measuring Work To measure work, you must know two things. First, you must know the amount of force used to move an object. The SI unit of force is the newton (N). Second, you must know the distance that the object moves. Distance is usually measured in meters (m).

Work is measured in newton-meters (N-m). Work is equal to force times distance. This can be written as a formula.

$$W = F \times d$$

In this equation, W is work, F is force, and d is distance. Suppose you lift an object weighing 50 N. Remember that weight is a force. You move the object a distance of 2 m. To calculate the amount of work done, multiply the force times the distance.

$$W = F \times d$$
$$W = 50 \text{ N} \times 2 \text{ m}$$
$$W = 100 \text{ N-m}$$

1 ▶ LIST: What two things must you know in order to measure work?

Unit of Work Scientists use a unit called a **joule** (J) to measure work. One joule of work is done when a force of 1 N moves an object a distance of 1 m. One joule is equal to 1 N-m of work.

2 ▶ IDENTIFY: What unit is used to measure work?

Direction of Force To measure work, you must measure the force applied in the direction of motion. This idea is illustrated in Figures 3-14 and 3-15. To lift a rock that weighs 50 N, you have to overcome gravity. You must apply a force of 50 N in an upward direction. Now, instead of lifting the rock, suppose you pulled the same 50-N rock a distance of 2 m along the ground. How much work have you done? Because you are overcoming friction instead of gravity, you will use less force—about 20 N. You must multiply this force times the distance moved. The work done equals 20 N × 2 m = 40 N-m, or 40 J.

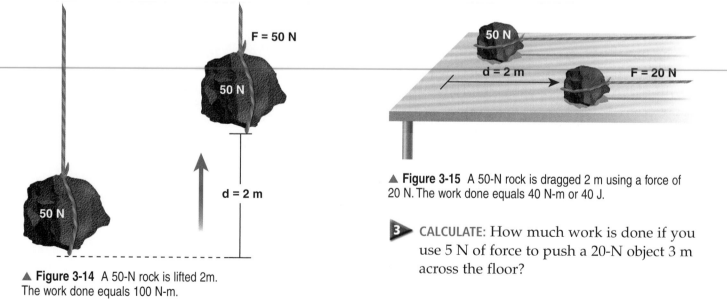

F = 50 N

50 N

d = 2 m

50 N

▲ **Figure 3-14** A 50-N rock is lifted 2m. The work done equals 100 N-m.

50 N

d = 2 m

F = 20 N

▲ **Figure 3-15** A 50-N rock is dragged 2 m using a force of 20 N. The work done equals 40 N-m or 40 J.

3 ▶ CALCULATE: How much work is done if you use 5 N of force to push a 20-N object 3 m across the floor?

✓ CHECKING CONCEPTS

1. The SI unit of force is the _____.
2. To measure work, you must know both force and _____.
3. Work can be measured in newton-_____.
4. The SI unit of work is the _____.
5. One joule is equal to 1 _____ .
6. To measure work, you must know the amount of force applied in the direction of _____.

💡 THINKING CRITICALLY

7. CALCULATE: How much work is done in each of the following examples? Show all of your calculations.
   a. A child uses 4 N of force to pull a wagon a distance of 2 m along a sidewalk.
   b. A construction worker uses 30 N of force to drag a toolbox a distance of 3 m.

8. COMPARE: In which case is more work done? Explain your answer.
   a. You lift a 40-N object 2 m straight up.
   b. You use 10 N of force to pull the same 40-N object 2 m across the floor.

Web InfoSearch

James Prescott Joule The metric unit of work, the joule, is named after James Prescott Joule. Joule was a physicist. He was born in England in 1818. Joule was one of the four scientists who helped state the law of conservation of energy. Joule's law is also named after him.

SEARCH: Write a short biography about James Prescott Joule and the scientific law named after him. Use the Internet to find out more. Start your search at www.conceptsandchallenges.com. Some key search words are **James Prescott Joule's Law.**

Hands-On Activity

MEASURING WORK

You will need a book, string, a spring scale, and a meter stick.

1. Tie a piece of string around a book.
2. Attach a spring scale to the book using the string.
3. Using the spring scale, lift the book a distance of 1 m. Record the amount of force shown on the spring scale. Calculate the amount of work done in joules.
4. Using the spring scale, pull the book at a constant velocity for a distance of 1 m across your desk or tabletop. Record the amount of force shown on the spring scale. Calculate and record the amount of work done in joules.

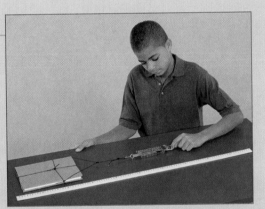

▲ STEP 4 Pull the book with the spring scale.

Practicing Your Skills

5. CALCULATE: How much work did you do when you lifted the book?
6. CALCULATE: How much work did you do when you pulled the book across your desk?
7. ANALYZE: Based on your calculations, does it require more work to lift an object or to drag it?

3-6 What is power?

Objective

Explain how to measure power.

Key Terms

power: amount of work done per unit of time

watt: SI unit of power; equal to 1 J/s

Power The amount of work done per unit of time is called **power.** The term *power* describes the rate at which you do work. Suppose you took 30 minutes to shovel snow from a sidewalk. Your neighbor used a snowblower to clear a sidewalk of the same size in 10 minutes. If you both did the same amount of work, which one of you used more power? Your neighbor who did the work in less time used more power.

▲ **Figure 3-16** Shoveling snow is hard work and takes a long time.

▲ **Figure 3-17** The power of a snowblower helps a person do the same amount of work in less time.

▶ DEFINE: What is power?

Measuring Power To measure power, you must measure two things. First, you must measure the amount of work done. Second, you must measure the time needed to do the work. The formula used to measure power is as follows:

$$power = work \div time$$

Recall that work is equal to force times distance. The formula for power can also be written as

$$power = (force \times distance) \div time.$$

▶ **2** IDENTIFY: What is the formula used to measure power?

Unit of Power The SI unit of power is the **watt** (W). Power is equal to work divided by time. The unit of work is the newton-meter, or joule. The unit of time is the second. Therefore, one watt (1 W) is equal to 1 N-m/s, or 1 J/s. The watt is named after James Watt. Watt was a Scottish engineer who built the first useful steam engine.

Large amounts of power are measured in kilowatts (kW). One kilowatt (1 kW) is equal to 1,000 W. You are probably familiar with watts and kilowatts as units of electric power. For example, light bulbs can be rated as 60 W, 100 W, or 250 W.

Electricity is not free. You have to pay for the electricity you use. How does the electric company know how much electricity your family uses? The electricity used in your house is measured by a meter like the one shown in Figure 3-18. The meter shows how many kilowatt-hours of electricity have been used.

▲ **Figure 3-18** An electric meter

▶ **3** HYPOTHESIZE: How does a 60-W light bulb differ from a 100-W light bulb?

✓ CHECKING CONCEPTS

1. The rate at which work is done is
   _____.

2. Power is the amount of work done per unit of
   _____.

3. To measure power, you must find the amount
   of _____ and the time needed.

4. Power = (force × _____)/time.

5. The SI unit of power is the _____.

6. One _____ is equal to 1,000 W.

7. One watt is equal to 1 N-m/s, or
   1 _____ /s.

8. The unit of power is named after James
   _____.

💡 THINKING CRITICALLY

9. **CALCULATE:** How much more power is used to
   move a weight of 500 N a distance of 20 m in
   5 s than is used to move a weight of 1,000 N a
   distance of 30 m in 30 sec?

10. **CALCULATE:** Find the amount of power used in
    each of the following examples. Show your
    calculations.

    a. You use a force of 10 N to move a box
       100 m in 10 seconds.

    b. An athlete lifting weights does 900 J of
       work in 1 second.

    c. A truck does 30,000 J of work in
       15 seconds.

    d. A furniture mover uses a force of 150 N to
       push a large trunk 5 m across the floor in
       5 seconds.

DESIGNING AN EXPERIMENT

*Design an experiment to solve the following problem.
Include a hypothesis, variables, a procedure, and a type
of data to collect and study.*

PROBLEM: How much power, in watts, do you
use when you climb a flight of stairs?

▲ **Figure 3-19** Measuring the power of one horse

How Do They Know That?

HORSEPOWER

You are probably familiar with the term
horsepower. Engines and motors are commonly
rated in horsepower. An automobile engine, for
example, may have about 100 horsepower. Where
does this unit of power come from?

James Watt was the first person to use the term
horsepower. Watt was a Scottish engineer and
inventor. In the 1760s, he built the first practical
steam engine. Watt wanted to use a unit of power
for his engine that would be familiar to most
people. He decided to use the power of a horse as the standard unit of power for
the steam engine. Watt found that a strong horse could lift a 746-N load a
distance of 1 m in 1 second. In other words, a horse produced 746 J/s of power.
Watt defined this amount of power as 1 horsepower (hp).

Today, the unit of power is the watt (W). It is named in honor of James Watt.
One watt is equal to 1 J/s. Therefore, 1 hp is equal to 746 W. Real horses are no
longer used as a standard of power.

Thinking Critically What types of machinery are still rated in horsepower?

LAB ACTIVITY
Studying Energy Changes in a Roller Coaster

BACKGROUND

Have you ever ridden a roller coaster? If you have, you were probably more concerned with fun than the science behind its operation. Roller coasters are machines that use potential and kinetic energy.

PURPOSE

In this activity, you will experiment with how roller coasters change potential energy into kinetic energy and back again several times.

PROCEDURE

1. Raise one end of the plastic tubing about $1\frac{1}{2}$ m above the floor. Tape this end to a bookcase or some other object so that it stays put. The tubing will serve as a roller-coaster track.

2. Use furniture, books, or other objects to make hills for your model roller coaster. Keep the track with its hills in a straight line. Do not include any turns. Tape the track securely so that it does not move.

Materials
Clear plastic tubing
Masking tape
Small ball bearing or glass bead
Meter stick
Pencil and paper

▲ **STEP 1** Tape one end of the track.

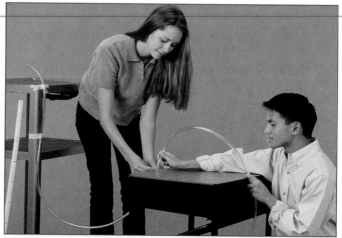

▲ **STEP 2** Create hills and valleys along one track.

3. Measure and record the height of the hills. Draw a sketch of your model roller coaster. Include your measurements.

4. Insert a ball bearing into the tubing at the high end. Test your model. Does the ball bearing reach the end of the track? Explain why. If necessary, adjust your design so that the ball bearing travels the entire length of the track.

▲ **STEP 4** Test your roller coaster

5. After testing your roller coaster, take it apart and make a new design for your track. You may wish to add curves or even some loops. Draw a sketch of your new design and test it. Record your observations.

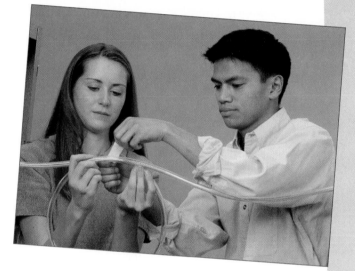
▲ **STEP 5** Make a new design for your track.

CONCLUSIONS

1. **OBSERVE AND DESCRIBE:** What happened to the ball bearing as you released it at the top of your roller-coaster track?

2. **ANALYZE:** Why does the first hill of a roller coaster have to be the highest hill?

3. **OBSERVE:** Compare the height of the hills as you move from the top to the bottom of the roller coaster.

4. **ANALYZE:** Why must the pattern of the hills be set up as it is?

5. **INFER:** Where on your roller coaster does the ball bearing have potential energy changing to kinetic energy? Where is kinetic energy changing to potential energy?

6. **INFER:** Where on your roller coaster does the ball bearing have the greatest potential energy? The least potential energy?

7. **INFER:** Where on your roller coaster does the ball bearing have the greatest kinetic energy? The least kinetic energy?

Chapter Summary

Lesson 3-1

- **Energy** is the ability to make something happen.
- There are two basic kinds of energy—potential energy and kinetic energy
- **Potential energy** is stored energy. **Kinetic energy** is energy of motion.

Lesson 3-2

- There are six main forms of energy: mechanical energy, electrical energy, electromagnetic energy, heat energy, chemical energy, and nuclear energy.

Lesson 3-3

- Energy can change from one form to another.
- When energy changes form, some of the energy is always changed into heat energy.
- The **law of conservation of energy** states that energy can never be created or destroyed but only changed in form.
- The total amount of matter and energy in the universe never changes.

Lesson 3-4

- **Work** is done when a force moves an object.
- For work to be done, the direction of the applied force must be the same as the direction of motion.

Lesson 3-5

- Work can be measured in newton-meters (N-m).
- The unit of work is the **joule** (J); 1 J = 1 N-m.
- When measuring work, you must measure the force applied in the direction of motion.

Lesson 3-6

- **Power** is the amount of work done per unit of time.
- Power = work/time, or (force × distance)/time.
- The SI unit of power is the **watt** (W).

Key Term Challenges

energy (p. 62)
joule (p. 72)
kinetic energy (p. 62)
law of conservation of energy (p. 66)

potential energy (p. 62)
power (p. 74)
thermal pollution (p. 66)
watt (p. 74)
work (p. 70)

MATCHING Write the Key Term from above that best matches each description.

1. stored energy
2. ability to make something happen
3. force times distance
4. energy of motion
5. metric unit of work
6. metric unit of power
7. work done per unit time

FILL IN Write the Key Term from above that best completes each statement.

8. The moving water in a waterfall has _____.

9. The _____ in a match is stored in the chemicals in the match head.

10. The faster you run, the more _____ you have.

11. Waste heat that escapes into the environment can cause _____.

12. The _____ states that energy cannot be made or destroyed but only changed in form.

13. When you use force to move an object, you are doing _____.

14. The _____ is the unit used to measure work.

15. The rate at which you do work is called _____.

16. The unit of power is the _____.

Content Challenges TEST PREP

MULTIPLE CHOICE **Write the letter of the term or phrase that best completes each statement.**

1. An object that is raised above the ground has
   a. heat energy.
   b. kinetic energy.
   c. potential energy.
   d. nuclear energy.

2. All moving objects have
   a. heat energy.
   b. kinetic energy.
   c. potential energy.
   d. nuclear energy.

3. Sound is a form of
   a. nuclear energy.
   b. electromagnetic energy.
   c. chemical energy.
   d. mechanical energy.

4. Electromagnetic energy includes X-rays and
   a. light.
   b. sound.
   c. chemicals.
   d. atoms.

5. An automobile engine changes chemical energy into
   a. electricity.
   b. nuclear energy.
   c. mechanical energy.
   d. light.

6. In the Sun, nuclear energy is changed into light energy and
   a. sound energy.
   b. chemical energy.
   c. electrical energy.
   d. heat energy.

7. Work = force times
   a. distance.
   b. mass.
   c. power.
   d. energy.

8. Work is measured in units called
   a. watts.
   b. meters.
   c. joules.
   d. newtons.

9. One watt is equal to
   a. 1 m/s.
   b. 1 J/s.
   c. 1 N/s.
   d. 1 kW/s.

TRUE/FALSE **Write *true* if the statement is true. If the statement is false, change the underlined term to make the statement true.**

10. Energy is the ability to do <u>work</u>.

11. Stored energy is <u>kinetic</u> energy.

12. <u>Potential</u> energy is energy of motion.

13. There are <u>six</u> main forms of energy.

14. The energy that holds atomic particles together is <u>nuclear</u> energy.

15. When energy changes form, some energy is always wasted as <u>sound</u>.

16. Energy <u>cannot</u> be made or destroyed.

17. Energy <u>cannot</u> be changed in form without work being done.

18. To measure work, you must know force and <u>time</u>.

19. For work to be done, an object must move in the <u>opposite</u> direction of the force applied to it.

20. In a light bulb, electrical energy is changed to light and <u>sound</u>.

WRITTEN RESPONSE Complete the exercises and answer each of the following questions in complete sentences.

1. **COMPARE:** Explain the difference between potential energy and kinetic energy.

2. **ANALYZE:** Describe the changes in potential and kinetic energy that take place in a swinging pendulum.

3. **EXPLAIN:** How does Einstein's equation, $E = mc^2$, support the law of conservation of energy?

4. **INFER:** How is it possible for energy to change form without any work being done?

5. **RELATE:** What is the relationship between work and power?

6. **INFER:** Why is gravitational potential energy called energy of position?

INTERPRETING A DIAGRAM Use Figures 3-20 and 3-21 to answer the following questions.

7. What is the weight of the object in Figure 3-20?

8. What distance is this object being lifted?

9. How much force is needed to lift this object?

10. How much work is being done to lift this object?

11. What is the weight of the object in Figure 3-21?

12. What distance is this object being pulled?

13. How much force is needed to pull this object?

14. How much work is being done to pull this object?

15. Is the amount of work being done in the two diagrams the same or different? Explain.

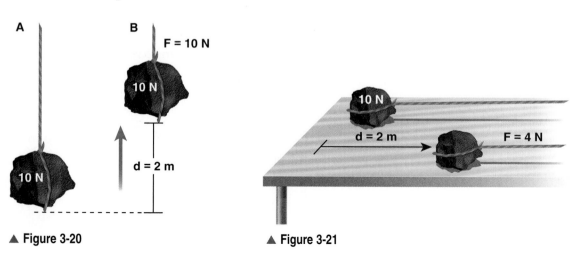

▲ Figure 3-20   ▲ Figure 3-21

Chapter 4 Machines

▲ **Figure 4-1** The Guggenheim Museum in New York City

The walkway around the inside walls of the Guggenheim Museum is one continuous ramp. The ramp is an inclined plane, a type of simple machine. You can walk along the ramp and view exhibits from the ground level to the top level without using stairs or an elevator.

▶Is walking up a ramp easier than walking up a staircase? Explain.

Contents

4-1 What is a simple machine?

INVESTIGATE

Using Machines
HANDS-ON ACTIVITY

1. Create a chart that lists the items in the classroom and at home that you use daily.
2. Check off each item you believe to be a machine.
3. Choose an item from your list. Tell a partner how it works as a machine.

THINK ABOUT IT: What are the different parts of your machine? How does it make your life easier?

STEP 3

Objective
Describe how machines make work easier.

Key Terms
machine: device that makes work easier

wheel and axle: two different-sized wheels that turn together around the same point

effort force: force applied to a machine

resistance force: force that opposes the effort force

mechanical advantage: number of times a machine multiplies the effort force

ideal mechanical advantage: mechanical advantage a machine would have with no friction

Simple Machines People use machines to make work easier. Did you ever try to take the lid off a can of paint using only your hands? If the lid is on very tight, your fingers cannot supply enough force to remove the lid. However, you can use a screwdriver as a lever to help you pry off the lid. A lever is an example of a simple machine. A **machine** is a device that makes work easier. Machines make work easier by changing the size, direction, or speed of a force.

Most machines are made up of two or more of the six simple machines shown in Figure 4-2. They are the lever, the pulley, the inclined plane, the screw, the wheel and axle, and the wedge.

▶ 1 NAME: What are the six simple machines?

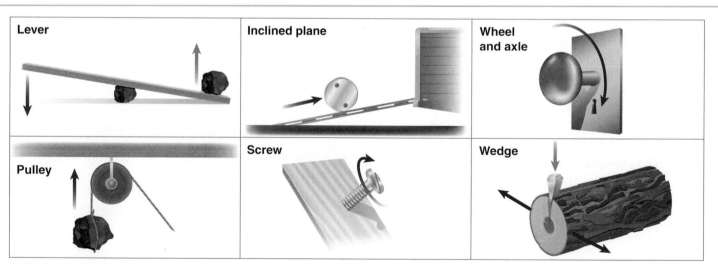

▲ **Figure 4-2** There are six simple machines.

Wheel and Axle The next time you open a door by turning a doorknob, stop for a minute and think. You have just used a simple machine called a wheel and axle. A **wheel and axle** is two different-sized wheels that turn together around the same point.

A wheel and axle is like a lever that moves in a circle. Many wheel-and-axle machines do not look like a wheel and axle. Figure 4-3 shows how a simple wrench can be a wheel and axle.

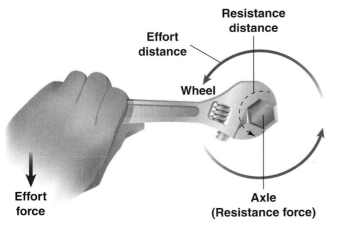

▲ **Figure 4-3** A wheel and axle machine

What makes a wheel and axle a simple machine? It makes work easier. It takes less force to turn the handle than it would to turn the axle by itself. You exert a small force on the handle, which exerts a larger force on the axle.

2 ► EXPLAIN: What makes a wheel and axle a simple machine?

Effort Force and Resistance Force The force you apply to a machine is called the **effort force.** For example, the force you apply to a wrench is the effort force. The force that opposes the effort force is called the **resistance force.** The nut is the resistance force you are trying to overcome when you turn the handle. A machine like the wrench lets you use a small force to overcome a large force.

Machines make work easier but they do not change the *amount* of work you do. When you use a machine, you often sacrifice distance to multiply your effort force. Look again at the wrench in Figure 4-3. You can see that the effort force applied to the wrench has to move a greater distance then does the resistance force you overcome when you turn the nut.

3 ► INFER: Does a wheel and axle change the size, direction, or speed of a force?

Mechanical Advantage Most machines help you do work by multiplying the effort force you apply to the machine. The number of times a machine multiplies the effort force is called the **mechanical advantage** (MA) of that machine. To find the mechanical advantage of a machine, divide the resistance force by the effort force. Use the example below to find the MA if you apply a force of 100 N to a machine to move a 1,500-N object.

> MA = resistance force ÷ effort force
> MA = 1,500 N ÷ 100 N
> MA = 15

4 ► DEFINE: What is mechanical advantage?

Ideal Mechanical Advantage The MA that a machine would have with no friction is known as the **ideal mechanical advantage** (IMA) of that machine. For example, the IMA of a single moveable pulley is 2. Such a pulley should multiply your effort force by 2. However, because of friction, and the weight of the pulley, the actual MA of the pulley will be less than 2.

5 ► DESCRIBE: What is the IMA of a machine?

✓ CHECKING CONCEPTS

1. How can you find the IMA of a machine?
2. What is resistance force?
3. What is force effort?

💡 THINKING CRITICALLY

4. INFER: How does friction affect the IMA of a machine?
5. ANALYZE: Can the actual MA of a machine ever be greater than its IMA? Explain.

BUILDING MATH SKILLS

Calculating Use the data in Figure 4-4 to find the MA of each simple machine.

	Effort force	Resistance force
a.	300 N	3,000 N
b.	160 N	1,600 N

▲ **Figure 4-4**

4-2 What is efficiency?

Objective
Explain how to find the efficiency of a machine.

Key Terms
work output: work done by a machine

work input: work done on a machine

efficiency (eh-FIHSH-uhn-see): ratio of work output to work input

Work Input and Work Output The work done by a machine is **work output.** Work output is equal to the resistance force times the distance through which the resistance force moves.

work output = resistance force × resistance distance

The work done on a machine is **work input.** The work input equals the effort force times the effort distance. The effort distance is the distance through which the force moves.

work input = effort force × effort distance

Machines cannot increase the amount of work done. As a result, the work output of a machine is never greater than the work input.

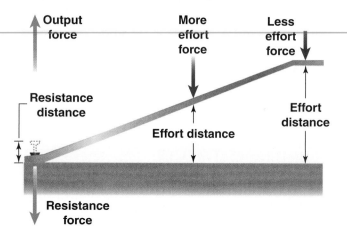

▲ **Figure 4-5** The longer the lever, the greater the effort distance. This reduces the needed effort force.

1 NAME: What is the work done by a machine called?

Efficiency Not all of the work put into a machine is changed into useful work. Some of the work input is used to overcome friction. This work is lost as heat energy. The **efficiency** of a machine is the ratio of work output to work input. It is usually expressed as a percentage.

You can find the percentage efficiency of a machine by dividing the work output by the work input and multiplying by 100.

percentage efficiency = work output ÷ work input × 100

Remember, the work done by a machine is always less than the work put into it. So, the efficiency of a machine is always less than 100%.

2 INFER: Why is the efficiency of a machine always less than 100%?

Increasing Efficiency The boat shown in Figure 4-6 is a racing shell. The oars used to move the shell through the water are levers. Each rower exerts an effort force on one end of an oar. As the oar moves through the water, it overcomes a resistance. The boat resists moving through the water because of the force of friction between the boat and the water.

Suppose some way could be found to reduce the force of friction between the boat and the water. This would decrease the resistance. Then, if each crew

▲ **Figure 4-6** Work is being done on the boat by eight simple machines.

member applies the same effort to the oars, the boat will move farther with each pull on the oars. In other words, the work input would remain the same, but the work output would be greater. This means that the efficiency has been increased.

3 ANALYZE: What is another way to increase efficiency besides decreasing the resistance force?

✓ CHECKING CONCEPTS

1. The work put out by a machine is _____ than the work put into a machine.

2. The efficiency of a machine is usually expressed as a _____.

3. Some of the work you put into a machine is always used to overcome _____.

4. The work put into a machine is equal to the effort force multiplied by the effort _____.

5. The efficiency of a machine always is less than _____.

💡 THINKING CRITICALLY

6. ANALYZE: Why can a machine not produce more work than is put into it?

7. HYPOTHESIZE: Why do you think many complex machines have very low efficiencies?

BUILDING MATH SKILLS

Calculating Complete the table in Figure 4-7 by calculating the missing value.

Work input	Work output	Efficiency
10 J	5 J	
20 J		40%
	30 J	60%
45 J	9 J	
	9 J	90%

▲ Figure 4-7

⚛ *Real-Life Science*

BICYCLING

The first successful bicycle was built by Baron Karl Von Drais de Sauerbrun in Karlsruhe, Germany, in 1817. This early bicycle had no pedals. Riders moved the bicycle forward by pushing backward against the ground with their feet. By 1839, a Scottish blacksmith, Kirkpatrick Macmillan, had added pedals. The modern bicycle began to be developed.

▲ **Figure 4-8** Modern bicycles are made to be more efficient.

In Europe and Asia, bicycles are major means of transportation. In the United States, bicycles are used mainly for recreation and exercise. Streets in many cities and towns have specially marked bicycle lanes. Bike paths are set aside in parks and in rural areas. All cyclists should be aware of traffic and safety rules before riding their bicycles in any of these areas.

Special bicycles have been developed for racing. These bicycles are made of strong, lightweight materials, such as alloys of titanium and carbon. Racing tires are very narrow to reduce weight and frictional drag. To further reduce friction, cyclists wear tight, specially designed clothing and streamlined helmets. These people take their sport very seriously.

Thinking Critically What features might a bicycle designed for off-road trails have?

4-3 How does a lever work?

INVESTIGATE

Using a Lever
HANDS-ON ACTIVITY

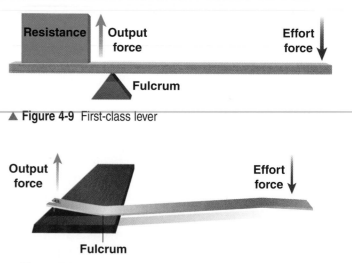

STEP 3

1. Balance a meter stick on a wood block at the 50-cm mark.
2. Place a 5 N weight on one end of the meter stick. Attach a spring scale to the other end as shown in the picture.
3. Pull down on the spring scale. Record the effort force needed to lift the weight.
4. Repeat Step 3 with the wood block at the 45-cm mark and again with the block at the 55-cm mark.

THINK ABOUT IT: Is it easier to lift the weight when the wood block is closer to the weight or farther from it? In which case did the resistance move farthest?

Objectives
Explain how a lever makes work easier. Describe the three classes of levers.

Key Terms
lever (LEHV-uhr): bar that is free to turn around a fixed point

fulcrum (FOOL-kruhm): fixed point around which a lever pivots or turns

Levers Have you ever used a shovel or a crowbar? If so, then you have used a lever. A **lever** is a bar that is free to turn around a fixed point. The fixed point on which a lever turns is called the **fulcrum.** A lever can make work easier by increasing force. Levers also change the direction of a force and the distance over which a force acts.

A lever has two parts—an effort arm and a resistance arm. The **effort arm** is the distance from the effort force to the fulcrum. The **resistance arm** is the distance from the resistance force to the fulcrum.

You can find the IMA of a lever by dividing the length of the effort arm by the length of the resistance arm.

IMA = effort arm length ÷ resistance arm length

▷ 1 EXPLAIN: How can you find the ideal mechanical advantage of a lever?

Classes of Levers There are three classes, or kinds, of levers. The classes of levers are based on the position of the resistance force, the effort force, and the fulcrum.

In a first-class lever, the fulcrum is between the effort force and the resistance force. These levers multiply force. The direction of the effort force is changed. Examples of first-class levers include crowbars, seesaws, and car jacks.

▲ Figure 4-9 First-class lever

▲ Figure 4-10 A crowbar is a first-class lever.

A second-class lever has the resistance between the effort force and the fulcrum. Second-class levers always multiply force. The direction of the effort force is not changed. Examples of second-class levers include wheelbarrows and nutcrackers.

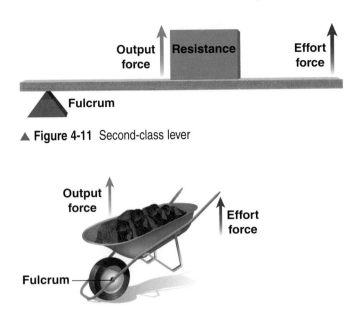

▲ **Figure 4-11** Second-class lever

▲ **Figure 4-12** A wheelbarrow is a second-class lever.

In a third-class lever, the effort force is between the fulcrum and the resistance force. These levers multiply the distance the resistance force moves, but the direction of the effort force is not changed. In third-class levers, the effort arm is always shorter than the resistance arm. Examples of third-class levers include shovels, baseball bats, and brooms.

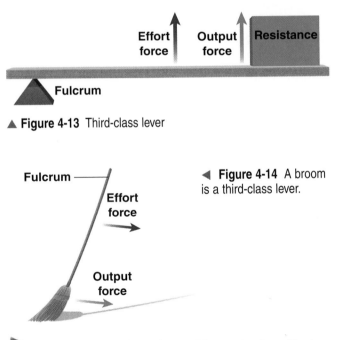

▲ **Figure 4-13** Third-class lever

◀ **Figure 4-14** A broom is a third-class lever.

2 IDENTIFY: In what class of lever is the effort force between the fulcrum and the resistance force?

1. The fixed point around which a lever turns is called the _____.
2. There are _____ classes of levers.
3. The ideal mechanical advantage of a lever is equal to the length of the effort arm divided by the length of the _____ arm.
4. In a _____-class lever, the effort force is between the fulcrum and the resistance force.
5. The resistance arm is the distance from the resistance force to the _____.

THINKING CRITICALLY

6. CALCULATE: What is the IMA of a lever with an effort arm 2 m long and a resistance arm 0.5 m long?
7. HYPOTHESIZE: How could you increase the IMA of a lever?
8. CLASSIFY: Classify each of the following as a first-, second-, or third-class lever: nutcracker, bottle opener, hammer, and hockey stick.

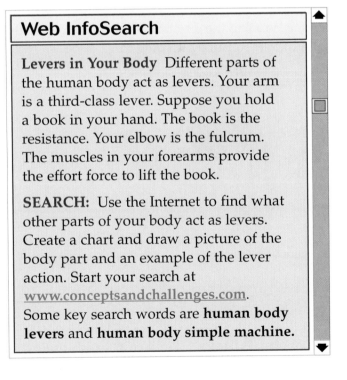

Web InfoSearch

Levers in Your Body Different parts of the human body act as levers. Your arm is a third-class lever. Suppose you hold a book in your hand. The book is the resistance. Your elbow is the fulcrum. The muscles in your forearms provide the effort force to lift the book.

SEARCH: Use the Internet to find what other parts of your body act as levers. Create a chart and draw a picture of the body part and an example of the lever action. Start your search at www.conceptsandchallenges.com. Some key search words are **human body levers** and **human body simple machine.**

4-4 How do pulleys work?

Objectives
Explain how pulleys make work easier. Compare fixed and movable pulleys.

Key Term
pulley: rope wrapped around a wheel

Pulleys Look at Figure 4-15. A pulley is being used to raise a bucket. A **pulley** is a rope wrapped around a wheel. Pulleys can change the direction of a force, the size of a force, or both. The pulley in Figure 4-15 changes the direction of a force. When the rope is pulled down, the bucket moves up.

 DEFINE: What is a pulley?

Fixed Pulleys A fixed pulley is attached to something that does not move. The pulley shown in Figure 4-15 is a fixed pulley. Fixed pulleys change the direction of the effort force. They do not increase the effort force. In a fixed pulley, the effort force is equal to the resistance force. As a result, the IMA of a fixed pulley is equal to 1.

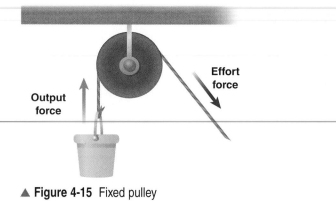

▲ **Figure 4-15** Fixed pulley

2 ► **EXPLAIN:** Why is the IMA of a fixed pulley equal to 1?

Movable Pulleys Unlike a fixed pulley, a movable pulley can move as the rope is being pulled through it. Figure 4-16 shows a single movable pulley. As the free end of the rope is pulled up, the pulley and its load also move up. A movable pulley does not change the direction of

the effort force. It does increase, or multiply, the size of the effort force. The IMA of a single movable pulley is equal to the number of supporting rope segments that lift the resistance. The IMA of a single movable pulley is 2. The effort distance is always twice the resistance distance.

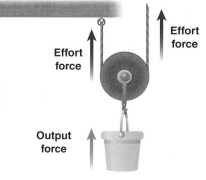

▲ **Figure 4-16** Movable pulley

3 ► **ANALYZE:** What is the IMA of the movable pulley in Figure 4-16? Why?

Pulley Systems A block and tackle is a pulley system. A pulley system is made up of both fixed and movable pulleys. The pulleys act together to increase the MA of the system. The IMA of a pulley system is equal to the number of supporting ropes. The rope attached to the fixed pulley is not counted. A block and tackle may have a large mechanical advantage, depending on the number of pulleys in the system.

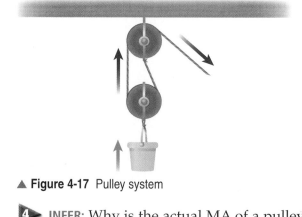

▲ **Figure 4-17** Pulley system

4 ► **INFER:** Why is the actual MA of a pulley system a lot smaller than its IMA?

✓ CHECKING CONCEPTS

1. A _____ pulley can increase the effort force.
2. The IMA of a fixed pulley is _____.
3. A _____ is an example of a pulley system.
4. The IMA of a pulley system with four supporting ropes is _____.
5. A _____ pulley can change only the direction of a force.

💡 THINKING CRITICALLY

6. **EXPLAIN:** Why is the IMA of a single movable pulley greater than that of a single fixed pulley?
7. **ANALYZE:** What kind of pulley is used to raise a flag to the top of a flagpole?
8. **INFER:** What happens to the actual mechanical advantage of a pulley system as more pulleys are added?

INTERPRETING VISUALS

Figure 4-18 shows a block and tackle.

9. What is the IMA of the block and tackle?

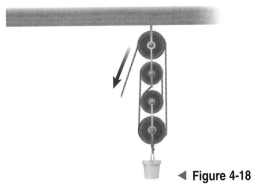

◀ **Figure 4-18**

BUILDING SCIENCE SKILLS

Modeling Design a machine that uses at least two types of pulleys. Your machine should have a practical use. Draw a diagram or build a working model of your machine. Label each pulley type. Explain how your machine works.

 Hands-On Activity

USING A MOVABLE PULLEY

You will need a spring scale, string, a movable pulley, a book, and tape.

1. Tie the string around the book. Attach the book to the spring scale.
2. Use the spring scale to lift the book. Record the effort force needed to lift the book.
3. Attach the movable pulley to the book and spring scale as shown.
4. Use the pulley to lift the book again. Record the effort force needed to lift the book.

Practicing Your Skills

5. **OBSERVE:** How much force was needed to lift the book without the pulley?
6. **OBSERVE:** How much force was needed to lift the book with the pulley?
7. **CALCULATE:** What is the actual MA of the movable pulley?

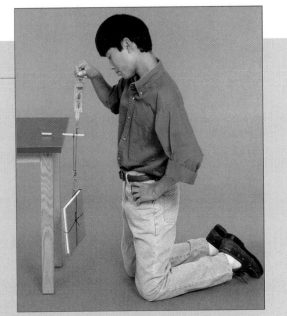

▲ **STEP 3** Attach the pulley to the book and spring scale.

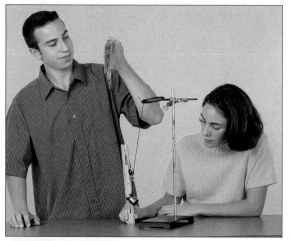

LAB ACTIVITY
Pulley Advantage

Materials

Ring stand and ring

Pulleys

Cord

Lifting mass

Spring scale –
250 g/5 N

Metric ruler

Calculator

BACKGROUND

Simple machines like levers, inclined planes, and pulleys make it seem like you get something for nothing. A difficult job becomes easier to do. What is really happening is a trade-off. The job is easier to do but it takes longer to do it. You can see this relationship with pulleys.

PURPOSE

In this activity, you will lift various masses with pulleys. You will then compare the effort forces and the distances the forces have to be exerted.

PROCEDURE

1. Copy the data table in Figure 4-19.

2. Make a single fixed pulley by attaching one pulley to the ring stand. Tie the cord to the mass and run it through the pulley. Tie a loop to the other end of the cord for hooking the spring scale.

3. Lift the weight off the tabletop slightly by pulling on the spring scale. Measure the force on the scale and record it in your data table.

4. Raise the weight 10 cm. Now, measure how far you had to pull the scale to raise the weight that distance. Record your answers in the data table.

5. Set up new pulley arrangements as shown in the picture labeled Step 5. Measure the forces and the distances as before.

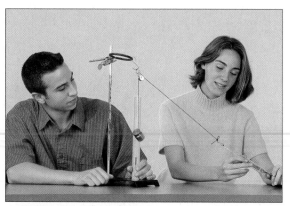

▲ **STEP 2** Set up the pulley.

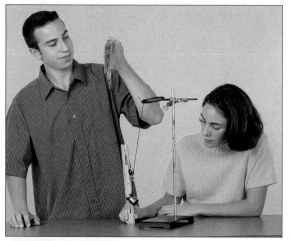

▲ **STEP 4** Measure the distances.

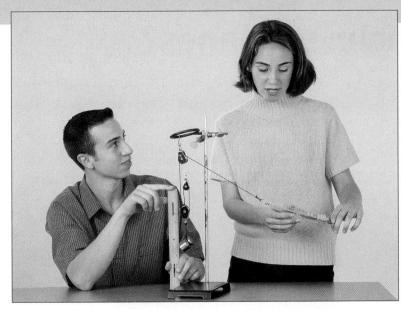

◀ STEP 5
Set up a pulley system.

Pulley Advantage

Setup	Number of Cords Holding Mass (mechanical advantage)	Lifting Mass	Lifting Force	Lifting Distance	Pulling Distance
1				10 cm	
2				10 cm	
3				10 cm	
4				10 cm	

▲ **Figure 4-19** Copy this chart and use it to record your observations.

CONCLUSIONS

1. **OBSERVE:** When you increased the number of supporting cords, what happened to the amount of force needed to lift the weight?

2. **OBSERVE:** When you increased the number of cords supporting the mass, what happened to the distance you had to exert the effort force?

3. **ANALYZE:** What is the relationship between force and distance when you increase the number of cords to two?

4. **INFER:** If you want to lift a very heavy mass with a pulley system, what should you do?

4-5 What are inclined planes?

Objective
Describe how an inclined plane makes work easier.

Key Term
inclined plane: slanted surface, or ramp

Inclined Planes A ramp is often used to help load barrels onto a truck. The barrels are rolled up the ramp onto the truck. The ramp is an inclined plane. The word *inclined* means "slanted." A plane is a flat surface. Therefore, an **inclined plane** is a slanted surface, or ramp. Inclined planes are simple machines that help make work easier.

 DEFINE: What is an inclined plane?

MA of an Inclined Plane An inclined plane makes work easier by changing the angle at which you have to exert force to lift resistance. Instead of lifting an object straight up against gravity, you push or pull the object up at an angle. Look at Figure 4-20 showing a man moving a box up an inclined plane. He is raising a 300-N box using only 100 N of effort force. In effect, the ramp has multiplied his effort force by 3. The MA of this ramp is 3.

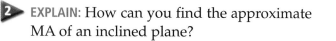
▲ **Figure 4-20** An inclined plane makes work easier.

You can find the IMA of an inclined plane by dividing its length by its height.

IMA = length ÷ height

IMA = 3 m ÷ 1 m

IMA = 3

2 EXPLAIN: How can you find the approximate MA of an inclined plane?

Wedges and Screws A wedge is a kind of inclined plane. A wedge is most often made of two inclined planes back-to-back. A knife blade and an axe are examples of wedges.

◀ **Figure 4-21** A wedge is two inclined planes back-to-back.

A screw is an inclined plane wrapped around a cylinder. A screw is like the steps wrapped around the center of a spiral staircase. Bolts are examples of screws.

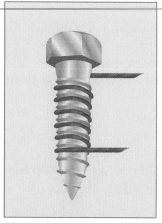
▲ **Figure 4-22** A screw is an inclined plane wrapped around a cylinder.

▲ **Figure 4-23** Screws are simple machines.

3 LIST: What are two examples of wedges?

1. A _____ is an inclined plane wrapped around a cylinder.

2. The IMA of an inclined plane is equal to its length divided by its _____.

3. A plane is a _____ surface.

4. Bolts are examples of _____.

5. An inclined plane _____ the size of the effort force.

6. A wedge is made up of _____ inclined planes.

💡 THINKING CRITICALLY

7. **HYPOTHESIZE:** How could you increase the IMA of an inclined plane?

8. **ANALYZE:** What happens to the IMA of an inclined plane if you increase the height?

INTERPRETING VISUALS

Figure 4-24 shows three ramps: A, B, and C.

9. Which ramp has the smallest IMA? Explain.

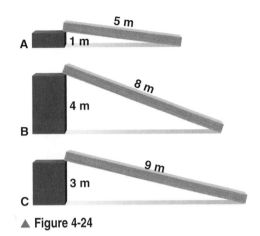

▲ **Figure 4-24**

⚛ *Hands-On Activity*

FINDING THE MA OF AN INCLINED PLANE

You will need a wooden board, a spring scale, string, a metric ruler, and three books.

1. Stack two books one on top of the other. Place one end of the wooden board on top of the books to make an inclined plane.

2. Use the metric ruler to measure the length and height of the inclined plane. Record your measurements.

3. Tie one end of the string around the third book. Tie the other end to the spring scale. Measure and record the weight of the book in newtons. The weight of the book is the resistance force, when no ramp is being used.

4. Use the spring scale to pull the book up the inclined plane. Record the effort force shown on the scale.

▲ **STEP 4** Use the spring scale to record the effort force.

Practicing Your Skills

5. **ANALYZE:** Find the IMA of the inclined plane using the formula IMA = length/height.

6. **CALCULATE:** Find the actual MA of the inclined plane using the formula IMA = resistance force/effort force.

7. **HYPOTHESIZE:** Why is the actual MA less than the IMA?

THE Big IDEA

How did the Egyptians build the Great Pyramid?

Is it possible to build something 480 ft tall using only simple machines? That is exactly what Khufu did, with a lot of help. The Egyptian Pharaoh Khufu had the Great Pyramid built at Giza 4,500 years ago. For most of recorded history, Khufu's pyramid was the world's largest building. It has a mass of almost 6 billion kilograms. It was originally 147 m tall; it covers an area of about ten football fields. Using only levers, wedges, inclined planes, muscle power, and engineering genius, Egyptian workers put more than 2 million huge blocks precisely in place to construct Khufu's monument.

Archeologists do not agree on exactly how the Great Pyramid and the other pyramids of Giza were constructed. However, they do agree that these structures were built with the simplest of machines. The workers may not even have had the wheel.

Copper wedges were used to cut the huge stone blocks. The stones were probably dragged to the construction site on greased sleds. They were moved up the pyramid on inclined planes. Some historians believe a single ramp was used to move the stones to the top. Others suggest that spiral ramps were built around the sides of the pyramid.

Positioning the top stones and the huge stones that form the inside chambers of the pyramid must have been very tricky. Expert use of levers and wedges was needed to set these stones. Look at the illustrations and text on these two pages. Then, follow the directions in the Science Log to learn more about "the big idea."◆

Wheels and Levers

Did the Egyptians have the wheel? Did they use levers? An ancient painting shows soldiers climbing a ladder on wheels. Others are using levers to move the structure. This is the only known image of a wheel from those times.

Wedges

Stonecutters used chisels made of bronze and copper. These wedge-shaped tools were used to carve fine details in the stone.

Inclined Planes

Scientists agree that the inclined plane was an important machine used to build the pyramids. They do not agree how they were built. Some experts think the stones were dragged up spiral ramps such as these. Other scientists think that a single, straight ramp was built from the bottom up to the top. Either way, we know they used inclined planes.

Figure 4-25
The Great Pyramid at Giza

Science Log

WRITING ACTIVITY

Research the process of cutting a stone for the Great Pyramid and putting it in place. In your science log, draw or describe the process in as much detail as you can. Be sure to explain which simple machines were probably used. Start your search at www.conceptsandchallenges.com.

4-6 What is a compound machine?

Objective
Name some compound machines.

Key Term
compound machine: machine that combines two simple machines or more

Compound Machines Most machines are made up of a combination of simple machines. Machines that combine two simple machines or more are called **compound machines.** Compound machines can do more complicated jobs than simple machines can. They also can have large MAs. The actual MA of a compound machine equals the product of the actual MAs of all of the simple machines that make it up.

▶ **DEFINE:** What is a compound machine?

Examples of Compound Machines Most of the machines you use every day are compound machines. For example, a pair of scissors is a compound machine. A pair of scissors is made up of two levers joined by a screw. The screw is the fulcrum of the levers. Each blade of a pair of scissors is a wedge.

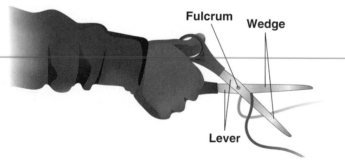
Fulcrum   Wedge

Lever

▲ **Figure 4-26** Scissors are compound machines.

A bicycle is another compound machine. What simple machines make up a bicycle? The wheels and pedals are wheels and axles. The pedals are attached to levers. The brakes, handlebars, and gearshift controls also are levers. The chains are pulleys. Screws are used in many places to hold parts of the bicycle together.

▲ **Figure 4-27** A bicycle is a compound machine.

▶ **IDENTIFY:** What are some simple machines in a bicycle?

People and Machines Humans have been using machines for hundreds of thousands of years. Early humans made simple tools from stone. Centuries later, agricultural societies used machines to water their crops, crush grain into flour, and cut wood to build homes.

During the Industrial Revolution, steam began to replace animals as a source of energy for machines. Many inventions during those years, such as the telephone and the telegraph, helped improve communication. We also learned how to heat our homes and power our machinery.

Today, fossil fuels and nuclear energy are used to operate modern machines. Modern machines take us anyplace in the world and to the Moon. In the future, new technology may make even more complex machines possible.

▲ Figure 4-28 The wheels of this train travel on a single track.

 NAME: What are two sources of energy for modern machines?

✔ CHECKING CONCEPTS

1. What are two simple machines that make up a pair of scissors?
2. What is a compound machine?
3. What type of simple machine are the wheels and handlebars of a bicycle?
4. On what does the MA of a compound machine depend?

💡 THINKING CRITICALLY

5. **COMPARE:** How does the MA of a compound machine compare with the MA of each of its simple machines?
6. **ANALYZE:** How does a bicycle make work easier?
7. **MODEL:** Draw a diagram of a pair of scissors. Label the simple machines that make up a pair of scissors on your diagram.

HEALTH AND SAFETY TIP

Machines are very helpful to people. However, if machines are not used properly, they can cause serious injury. It is important to use proper safety precautions when you use any kind of machine. Helmets, kneepads, and goggles are all safety items you might need. Different machines require different precautions. Choose a machine you are interested in and find out the safety precautions and safety equipment needed to use it. Make a poster that illustrates "Machine Safety."

Science and Technology

ROBOTIC MACHINES

Robots are mechanical workers. Most robots are built to do special jobs. Using robots instead of human workers has some advantages. Robots can work 24 hours a day without resting. They can do the same job over and over without getting tired or bored.

More importantly, robots can work under conditions that would not be safe for humans. The Sewer Access Module robot, or SAM, was designed to do maintenance work in sewers. Today, it is also used to lay fiber-optic cable lines in the sewer.

▲ Figure 4-29 This robot is used to clean sewers.

Robots are used in a wide variety of places. Some surgeons use robots in the operating room to perform open-heart surgeries. The robot can grip, cut, and sew arteries and valves. Surgeons view the heart on a video monitor. They control the robot's movements with joysticks and foot pedals. Because robotic surgery requires a smaller incision, a patient's recovery time is faster.

Thinking Critically For what other types of jobs could robots be used?

Chapter Summary

Lesson 4-1

- **Machines** make work easier by changing the size, direction, or speed of a force.
- The force you apply to a machine is the **effort force,** and the force that opposes the effort force is the **resistance force.**
- **Mechanical advantage** is the number of times a machine multiplies the effort force. It is equal to the resistance force divided by the effort force.
- There are six kinds of simple machines.

Lesson 4-2

- The work done by a machine is **work output.** The work done on a machine is **work input.** A machine's **efficiency** is a ratio of work output to work input.

Lesson 4-3

- A **lever** is a bar that is free to turn around a fixed point. A lever has two parts called an effort arm and a resistance arm. The IMA of a lever is equal to the length of the effort arm divided by the length of the resistance arm.
- Levers are divided into three classes according to the position of the effort force, the resistance force, and the **fulcrum.**

Lesson 4-4

- A **pulley** is a rope wrapped around a wheel.
- Fixed pulleys change the direction of the effort force. Movable pulleys increase the size of the effort force. A pulley system is made up of fixed and movable pulleys.

Lesson 4-5

- An **inclined plane** is a slanted surface, or ramp.
- The IMA of an inclined plane is equal to its length divided by its height.
- A wedge is often two inclined planes back-to-back. A screw is an inclined plane wrapped around a cylinder.

Lesson 4-6

- A **compound machine** is composed of two or more simple machines.

Key Term Challenges

compound machine (p. 96)
efficiency (p. 84)
effort force (p. 82)
fulcrum (p. 86)
ideal mechanical advantage (p. 82)
inclined plane (p. 92)
lever (p. 86)
machine (p. 82)
mechanical advantage (p. 82)
pulley (p. 88)
resistance force (p. 82)
wheel and axle (p. 82)
work input (p. 84)
work output (p. 84)

MATCHING Write the Key Term from above that best matches each description.

1. force applied to a machine
2. rope wrapped around a wheel
3. slanted surface
4. work done by a machine
5. force that opposes the effort force
6. work done on a machine
7. point that a lever turns around

APPLYING DEFINITIONS Explain the difference between the words in each pair. Write your answers in complete sentences.

8. lever, fulcrum
9. simple machine, compound machine
10. mechanical advantage, efficiency
11. work input, work output
12. effort force, resistance force

Content Challenges TEST PREP

MULTIPLE CHOICE **Write the letter of the term or phrase that best completes each statement.**

1. Machines make work easier by changing a force's
   a. size.
   b. direction.
   c. speed.
   d. size, direction, or speed.

2. A machine with an actual MA of 10 multiplies the effort force
   a. 15 times.
   b. 10 times.
   c. 10%.
   d. 15%.

3. The efficiency of a machine is always less than
   a. 100%.
   b. the mechanical advantage.
   c. work output.
   d. work input.

4. If the percentage efficiency of a machine is 60% and the work input is 50 N-m, what will be the work output?
   a. 160 N-m.
   b. 60 N-m.
   c. 30 N-m.
   d. 100 N-m.

5. In a first-class lever, the fulcrum is between the effort force and
   a. the effort arm.
   b. the resistance arm.
   c. the resistance force.
   d. none of these

6. A wheelbarrow is an example of a
   a. first-class lever.
   b. second-class lever.
   c. third-class lever.
   d. wheel and axle.

7. A block and tackle is an example of a
   a. lever.
   b. pulley.
   c. pulley system.
   d. wheel and axle.

8. The IMA of a pulley system with six ropes supporting the load is
   a. 6.
   b. 3.
   c. 60%.
   d. 1.

9. An inclined plane makes work easier by increasing a force's
   a. direction.
   b. speed.
   c. MA.
   d. size.

10. If you use 50 N of force to push a box weighing 200 N up an inclined plane, the MA of the inclined plane is
   a. 50.
   b. 150.
   c. 4.
   d. 0.215.

FILL IN **Write the term or phrase that best completes each statement.**

11. People use _____ to make work easier.

12. The efficiency of a machine is equal to the _____ divided by the work input.

13. Some of the work put into a machine is used to overcome _____.

14. The _____ of a lever is the distance from the resistance force to the fulcrum.

15. A pulley can change either the size or the _____ of a force.

Concept Challenges TEST PREP

WRITTEN RESPONSE Complete the exercises and answer each of the following questions in complete sentences.

1. **RELATE:** Why is work input equal to the effort force times the effort distance?

2. **HYPOTHESIZE:** Why do you think compound machines are sometimes called complex machines?

3. **HYPOTHESIZE:** A perpetual motion machine would have more than 100% efficiency. Could such a machine ever be built? Explain your answer.

4. **EVALUATE:** Two piano movers want to raise a piano to the fifth floor of an apartment building. Should they use a fixed pulley, a movable pulley, or a block and tackle to make the work easier? Explain.

INTERPRETING A DIAGRAM Use Figure 4-30 to answer the following questions.

5. What is the length of the effort arm of this lever?

6. What is the length of the resistance arm?

7. What is the IMA of this lever?

8. What is the output force in this diagram?

9. How much effort force would be needed to produce the output force?

10. Is this lever a first-, second-, or third-class lever? Explain.

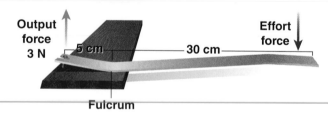

Output force 3 N — 5 cm — 30 cm — Effort force — Fulcrum

▲ Figure 4-30

Appendix A Metric System

The Metric System and SI Units

The metric system is an international system of measurement based on units of ten. More than 90% of the nations of the world use the metric system. In the United States, both the English system and the metric system are used.

The *Système International*, or SI, has been used as the international measurement system since 1960. The SI is a modernized version of the metric system. Like the metric system, the SI is a decimal system based on units of ten. When you want to change from one unit in the metric system to another unit, you multiply or divide by a multiple of ten.

- When you change from a smaller unit to a larger unit, you divide.

- When you change from a larger unit to a smaller unit, you multiply.

METRIC UNITS		
LENGTH	SYMBOL	RELATIONSHIP
kilometer	km	1 km = 1,000 m
meter	m	1 m = 100 cm
centimeter	cm	1 cm = 10 mm
millimeter	mm	1 mm = 0.1 cm
AREA	SYMBOL	
square kilometer	km^2	$1 \; km^2 = 1,000,000 \; m^2$
square meter	m^2	$1 \; m^2 = 1,000,000 \; mm^2$
square centimeter	cm^2	$1 \; cm^2 = 0.0001 \; m^2$
square millimeter	mm^2	$1 \; mm^2 = 0.000001 \; m^2$
VOLUME	SYMBOL	
cubic meter	m^3	$1 \; m^3 = 1,000,000 \; cm^3$
cubic centimeter	cm^3	$1 \; cm^3 = 0.000001 \; m^3$
liter	L	1 L = 1,000 mL
milliliter	mL	1 mL = 0.001 L
MASS	SYMBOL	
metric ton	t	1 t = 1,000 kg
kilogram	kg	1 kg = 1,000 g
gram	g	1 g = 1,000 mg
centigram	cg	1 cg = 10 mg
milligram	mg	1 mg = 0.001 g
TEMPERATURE	SYMBOL	
Kelvin	K	
degree Celsius	°C	

▲ Figure 1

COMMON METRIC PREFIXES			
micro-	0.000001 or 1/1,000,000	deka-	10
milli-	0.001 or 1/1,000	hecto-	100
centi-	0.01 or 1/100	kilo-	1,000
deci-	0.1 or 1/10	mega-	1,000,000

▲ Figure 2

METRIC-STANDARD EQUIVALENTS	
SI to English	English to SI
LENGTH	
1 kilometer = 0.621 mile (mi)	1 mi = 1.61 km
1 meter = 1.094 yards (yd)	1 yd = 0.914 m
1 meter = 3.28 feet (ft)	1 ft = 0.305 m
1 centimeter = 0.394 inch (in.)	1 in. = 2.54 cm
1 millimeter = 0.039 inch	1 in. = 25.4 mm
AREA	
1 square kilometer = 0.3861 square mile	$1 \; mi^2 = 2.590 \; km^2$
1 square meter = 1.1960 square yards	$1 \; yd^2 = 0.8361 \; m^2$
1 square meter = 10.763 square feet	$1 \; ft^2 = 0.0929 \; m^2$
1 square centimeter = 0.155 square inch	$1 \; in.^2 = 6.452 \; cm^2$
VOLUME	
1 cubic meter = 1.3080 cubic yards	$1 \; yd^3 = 0.7646 \; m^3$
1 cubic meter = 35.315 cubic feet	$1 \; ft^3 = 0.0283 \; m^3$
1 cubic centimeter = 0.0610 cubic inch	$1 \; in.^3 = 16.39 \; cm^3$
1 liter = 0.2642 gallon (gal)	1 gal = 3.79 L
1 liter = 1.06 quarts (qt)	1 qt = 0.946 L
1 liter = 2.11 pints (pt)	1 pt = 0.47 L
1 milliliter = 0.034 fluid ounce (fl oz)	1 fl oz = 29.57 mL
MASS	
1 metric ton = 0.984 ton	1 ton = 1.016 t
1 kilogram = 2.205 pounds (lb)	1 lb = 0.4536 kg
1 gram = 0.0353 ounce (oz)	1 oz = 28.35 g
TEMPERATURE	
Celsius = 5/9(°F − 32)	Fahrenheit = 9/5°C + 32
0°C = 32°F (Freezing point of water)	72°F = 22°C (Room temperature)
100°C = 212°F (Boiling point of water)	98.6°F = 37°C (Human body temperature)
Kelvin = (°F + 459.67)/1.8	Fahrenheit = (K × 1.8) − 459.67

▲ Figure 3

Appendix B   Science Terms

Analyzing Science Terms

You can often unlock the meaning of an unfamiliar science term by analyzing its word parts. Prefixes and suffixes, for example, each carry a meaning that comes from a word root. This word root usually comes from the Latin or Greek language. The following list of prefixes and suffixes provides clues to the meaning of many science terms.

WORD PART	MEANING	EXAMPLE
-ate	salt of an acid	nitrate
bar-, baro-	weight, pressure	barometer
bi-	two	binary
carbo-	containing carbon	carbonate
co-	with, together	coagulation
de-	remove from	decomposition
electro-	electricity	electrolyte
-graph	write	thermograph
hydro-	water, containing hydrogen	hydrometer, hydrocarbon
-ide	binary compound	sulfide
in-	not	insoluble
-logy	study of	cosmology
-lysis	decomposition	electrolysis
magneto-	magnetism	magnetosphere
-meter	measuring device	manometer
non-	not	nonmetal
photo-	light	photoelectric
poly-	many	polyatomic
re-	again, back	reflection
-sonic	sound	supersonic
-sphere	ball, globe	magnetosphere
sub-	under, beneath	subscript
super-	above, more than	supersonic
therm-, thermo-	heat	thermometer
trans-	across, beyond	transparent
ultra-	beyond	ultrasound
un-	not	unsaturated

▲ Figure 4

Appendix C Mathematics Review

Adding Integers

You can add integers with unlike signs on a number line.

Add $^-5 + {}^+7$

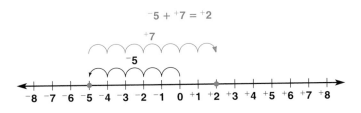

$$^-5 + {}^+7 = {}^+2$$

Subtracting Integers

To subtract an integer, add its opposite.

Subtract $^-6 - {}^+2$

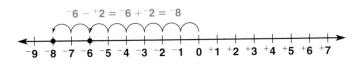

$$^-6 - {}^+2 = {}^-6 + {}^-2 = {}^-8$$

Multiplying Integers

When you multiply integers, you must decide if the answer is positive or negative.

If the signs of the integers are the same, the product is positive.

$$^+5 \times {}^+4 = {}^+20$$
$$^-5 \times {}^-4 = {}^+20$$

If the signs of the integers are different, the product is negative.

$$^+5 \times {}^-4 = {}^-20$$
$$^-5 \times {}^+4 = {}^-20$$

Dividing Integers

The rules for dividing integers are the same as the rules for multiplying integers.

If the signs of the integers are the same, the quotient is positive.

$$^-36 \div {}^-9 = {}^+4$$
$$^+36 \div {}^+9 = {}^+4$$

If the signs of the integers are different, the quotient is negative.

$$^-36 \div {}^+9 = {}^-4$$
$$^+36 \div {}^-9 = {}^-4$$

Solving an Equation

To solve an equation, find the value of the variable that makes the equation true.

Is $b = 3$ the solution to the equation?

$$4b = 12$$

Replace b with 3 in the equation.

$$4 \times 3 = 12$$
$$12 = 12$$

Yes, $b = 3$ is the solution to the equation.

Adding and Subtracting Decimals

When adding or subtracting decimals, always be sure to line up the decimal points correctly.

Add 3.4 km, 20.95 km, and 153.6 km.

$$\begin{array}{r} 3.4 \\ 20.95 \\ + \ 153.6 \\ \hline 177.95 \text{ km} \end{array}$$

Subtract 13.5 mL from 35.75 mL.

$$\begin{array}{r} 35.75 \\ - \ 13.5 \\ \hline 22.25 \text{ mL} \end{array}$$

Multiplying and Dividing Decimals

When multiplying or dividing decimals, it is not necessary to line up the decimal points.

Multiply 0.5 N by 11.25 m to find the amount of work done in joules.

$W = F \times d$

$W = 0.5 \text{ N} \times 11.25 \text{ m}$

$W = 5.625 \text{ J}$

Notice that the number of places to the right of the decimal point in the answer is equal to the sum of the places to the right of the decimal point in the numbers being multiplied.

Divide 4.05 m by 0.5 m to find the mechanical advantage of a lever.

MA = effort arm length/resistance arm length

MA = 4.05 m/0.5 m

MA = 8.1

When dividing a decimal by another decimal, you must first change the divisor to a whole number. For example, change 0.5 to 5 by moving the decimal point one place to the right. You must also change the dividend by moving the decimal point one place to the right. The result is $40.5 \div 5 = 8.1$.

Changing a Decimal to a Percent

To change a decimal to a percent, multiply the decimal by 100%.

Find the efficiency of a machine if the work output is 5 J and the work input is 10 J.

Efficiency = work output ÷ work input × 100%

Efficiency = 5 J ÷ 10 J × 100%

Efficiency = 0.5 × 100%

Efficiency = 50%

Notice that when you multiply 0.5 by 100%, the decimal point moves two places to the right.

Measuring Angles

Use a protractor to measure an angle. Place the center of the protractor's straight edge on the vertex. One ray must pass through 0°.

Angle ABC measures 75°.

Solving Word Problems

To solve distance problems, you can use $d = r \times t$ or $d = rt$.

The Smiths drove 220 miles at an average speed of 55 miles per hour. How long did the trip take?

PLAN

Substitute the values you know into the equation $d = r \times t$.

Then solve.

DO

$$220 = 55t$$

$$220 \div 55 = 55t \div 55$$

$$4 = t$$

SOLUTION

The trip took 4 hours.

Appendix D   Mathematical Formulas

MATTER

Density

Density is measured in grams per cubic centimeter (g/cm^3).

> Density = mass ÷ volume
>
> or
>
> D = m ÷ v
>
> or
>
> $D = \dfrac{m}{v}$

Specific Gravity

Specific gravity has no units of measure.

To find the specific gravity of a sample of matter, divide the density of the sample by the density of water (1.0 g/cm^3).

> Specific gravity = x g/cm^3 ÷ 1.0 g/cm^3

Area

1. The area of a rectangle is found by multiplying the length (*l*) by the width (*w*). Answers are given in square units (cm^2).

> A = l × w

2. The area of a square is found by squaring the side.

> A = s^2

3. The area of a circle is found by multiplying pi by the radius squared (*r*^{2}).

> (π ≈ 3.14) × *r*^{2}
> A = π *r*^{2}

Volume of a Solid Shape

1. The volume of a cylinder is found by multiplying pi by the radius squared (*r*^{2}) by the height (*h*).

> V = π × *r*^{2} × h

2. To find the volume of a rectangular prism or cube, multiply the length by the width by the height.

> V = l × w × h

3. The volume of a sphere is found by multiplying 4/3 by pi by the radius cubed (*r*^{3}).

> V = 4/3 × π × *r*^{3}

WORK

Mechanical Advantage

1. Mechanical Advantage = resistance force ÷ effort force

> or
>
> $MA = \dfrac{\text{resistance force}}{\text{effort force}} = \dfrac{F_r}{F_e}$
>
> or
>
> $MA = F_r ÷ F_e$

2. MA (of an inclined plane) = length × height

> MA = l × h
> MA = lh

Efficiency

Efficiency is expressed as a percentage.

> Efficiency = Work output ÷ Work input × 100%
>
> or
>
> $E = \dfrac{W_{out}}{W_{in}} × 100\%$
>
> or
>
> $E = W_{out} ÷ W_{in} × 100\%$

Work

Work is measured in joules (J). One joule equals one newton-meter (N-m).

> W = force × distance
>
> or
>
> W = F × d

Power

Power is measured in watts (W).

One watt is equal to one joule per second (J/s).

> Power = Work ÷ time
>
> or
>
> $P = \dfrac{W}{t}$
>
> or
>
> P = W ÷ t

Appendix D Mathematical Formulas (continued)

FORCE AND MOTION

Speed

Velocity is speed and direction.

1. Speed = distance ÷ time

   or

   $$v = \frac{d}{t}$$

   or

   $$v = d \div t$$

2. Change in velocity = final velocity − initial velocity
3. Acceleration = change in velocity ÷ time

Distance

Distance traveled is measured in miles or kilometers per hour (mph or km/h).

Distance = rate × time

or

$$d = r \times t$$

or

$$d = rt$$

Momentum

Momentum = mass × velocity

Force

Force = mass × acceleration

Force = pressure × area

Pressure

Pressure is expressed in pascals.

$$1 \text{ Pa} = 1 \frac{N}{m^2}$$

Pressure = force ÷ area

or

$$P = \frac{F}{a}$$

or

$$P = F \div a$$

ENERGY

Energy

Energy = mass × speed of light^2

or

$$E = m \times c^2$$

or

$$E = mc^2$$

Ohm's Law

Current is measured in amperes, or amps.

Current = voltage ÷ resistance

or

$$I = \frac{V}{R}$$

or

$$I = V \div R$$

Gravitational Potential Energy

PE = weight × height

PE (N-m) = N × m

Speed of a Wave

Velocity = frequency × wavelength

$$v = f \times D$$

Glossary

Pronunciation and syllabication have been derived from *Webster's New World Dictionary*, Second College Edition, Revised School Printing (Prentice Hall, 1985). Syllables printed in capital letters are given primary stress. (Numbers in parentheses indicate the page number, or page numbers, on which the term is defined.)

PRONUNCIATION KEY					
Symbol	**Example**	**Respelling**	**Symbol**	**Example**	**Respelling**
a	transpiration	(tran-spuh-RAY-shuhn)	oh	biome	(BY-ohm)
ah	composite	(kuhm-PAHZ-iht)	oi	asteroid	(AS-tuhr-oid)
aw	atoll	(A-tawl)	oo	altitude	(AL-tuh-tood)
ay	abrasion	(uh-BRAY-zhuhn)	ow	compound	(KAHM-pownd)
ch	leaching	(LEECH-ing)	s	satellite	(SAT-uhl-yt)
eh	chemical	(KEHM-i-kuhl)	sh	specialization	(spehsh-uhl-ih-ZAY-shuhn)
ee	equinox	(EE-kwih-nahks)	th	thermocline	(THUR-muh-klyn)
f	hemisphere	(HEHM-ih-sfeer)	th	weathering	(WEHTH-uhr-ing)
g	galaxy	(GAL-uhk-see)	uh	volcanism	(VAHL-kuh-nihzm)
ih	anticline	(AN-tih-klyn)	y, eye	anticline, isobar	(AN-tih-klyn), (EYE-soh-bahr)
j	geologic	(jee-uh-LAHJ-ihk)	yoo	cumulus	(KYOOM-yuh-luhs)
k	current	(KUR-uhnt)	z	deposition	(dehp-uh-ZIHSH-uhn)
ks	axis	(AK-sihs)	zh	erosion	(e-ROH-zhuhn)

A

acceleration (ak-sehl-uh-RAY-shuhn): rate of change in velocity over time (p. 44)

action force: force acting in one direction (p. 54)

air pressure: pressure caused by the force exerted by Earth's atmosphere (p. 32)

air resistance: force that opposes the movement of an object in air (p. 28)

average speed: total distance traveled divided by the time it takes to travel that distance (p. 42)

B

balanced forces: forces that are equal in size but opposite in direction (p. 16)

barometer (buh-RAHM-uht-uhr): instrument used to measure air pressure (p. 32)

Bernoulli's principle: as the speed of a fluid increases, its pressure decreases (p. 32)

C

communication: sharing information (p. 8)

compound machine: machine that combines two simple machines or more (p. 96)

constant: something that does not change (p. 11)

controlled experiment: experiment in which all the conditions except one are kept constant (p. 11)

D

data: information you collect when you observe something (p. 3)

E

efficiency (eh-FIHSH-uhn-see): ratio of work output to work input (p. 84)

effort force: force applied to a machine (p. 82)

energy: ability to make something happen (p. 62)

F

force: a push or a pull (p. 16)

friction: force that opposes the motion of an object (p. 24)

fulcrum (FOOL-kruhm): fixed point around which a lever pivots or turns (p. 86)

G

gram: basic unit of mass (p. 4)

gravity: force of attraction between all objects in the universe (p. 18)

H

hypothesis: suggested answer to a question or problem (p. 10)

I

ideal mechanical advantage: mechanical advantage a machine would have with no friction (p. 82)

inclined plane: slanted surface, or ramp (p. 92)

inertia (ihn-UR-shuh): tendency of an object to stay at rest or in motion (p. 50)

J

joule (JOOL): SI unit of work; equal to 1 N-m (newton-meter) (p. 72)

K

kinetic (kih-NEHT-ihk) **energy:** energy of motion (p. 62)

L

law of conservation of energy: energy cannot be made or destroyed but only changed in form (p. 66)

law of conservation of momentum: total momentum of any isolated system always remains the same (p. 46)

lever (LEHV-uhr): bar that is free to turn around a fixed point (p. 86)

liter: basic unit of liquid volume (p. 4)

lubricants (LOO-brih-kuhnts): substances that reduce friction (p. 26)

M

machine: device that makes work easier (p. 82)

mass: amount of matter in something (p. 4)

mechanical advantage (MA): number of times a machine multiplies the effort force (p. 82)

meniscus: curve at the surface of a liquid in a thin tube (p. 4)

meter: basic unit of length or distance (p. 4)

model: tool scientists use to represent an object or a process (p. 3)

momentum: property of all moving objects (p. 46)

motion: change in position relative to some fixed object or place (p. 42)

N

newton: SI unit of force (pp. 22, 52)

P

potential (puh-TEHN-shuhl) **energy:** stored energy (p. 62)

power: amount of work done per unit of time (p. 74)

pressure: force per unit of area (p. 30)

pulley: rope wrapped around a wheel (p. 88)

R

reaction force: force acting in the opposite direction (p. 54)

resistance force: force that opposes the effort force (p. 82)

S

simulation: computer model that usually shows a process (p. 3)

speed: distance traveled per unit of time (p. 42)

T

terminal velocity: speed at which air resistance and gravity acting on a falling object are equal (p. 28)

temperature: measurement of the amount of heat energy something contains (p. 4)

theory: set of hypotheses that have been supported by testing over and over again (p. 10)

thermal pollution: damage that occurs when waste heat enters the environment (p. 66)

U

unbalanced forces: forces that cause a change in the motion of an object (p. 16)

unit: amount used to measure something (p. 4)

V

vacuum: space where no matter exists (p. 28)

variable: anything that can affect the outcome of an experiment (p. 11)

velocity (vuh-LAHS-uh-tee): speed and direction (p. 44)

volume: amount of space an object takes up (p. 4)

W

watt: SI unit of power; equal to 1 J/s (p. 74)

wheel and axle: two different-sized wheels that turn together around the same point (p. 82)

work: force exerted through a distance (p. 70)

work input: work done on a machine (p. 84)

work output: work done by a machine (p. 84)

Index

P

people, machines and, 96
planets, orbiting, 20–21
potential energy, 62, 66
  changing, 66
power, 74–75
  measuring, 74
  unit of, 74
pressure, 30–31
  changing, 30
  in nature, 30
  versus depth, 34
protective headgear, 48
pulley advantage, 90–91
pulleys, 82, 88–89, 96
  fixed, 88
  movable, 88
pulley systems, 88–89

R

radio waves, 64
ramp, 81
reaction force, 83, 87
resistance, 54–55
resistance arm, 86
resistance force, 83
rockets, 55
rolling friction, 26

S

scientific method, 29
screws, 82, 92, 96
scuba diving, 35
simple machines, 82, 90
SI unit of force, 22
skiing, 27
snorkeling, 35
solar energy, 68
sound energy, 65
speed
  average, 42–43
  constant, 42
  instantaneous, 42
  motion and, 42
sports
  inertia and, 51
  work and, 71
spring scales, 22–23
  types of, 22
  using, 22

steam, 96
streamlining, 33
  effects of, 29
submarine, 34

T

terminal velocity, 28
thermal pollution, 67
thrust, 33
tornadoes, 71

U

unbalanced forces, 16, 50, 52
universal gravitation, 18

V

vacuum, 28
velocity, 44
VentureStar, 55
volcanoes, 30

W

waste heat, 67
water pressure, 34–35
watt, 74–75
Watt, James, 74–75
wedges, 82, 92, 94, 96
weight
  as force, 22
wheel, 94
wheel and axle, 82–83
wind, 63, 68–69, 71
windmills, 68, 71
wing shape, air pressure and, 33
work, 70–71
  energy and, 70
  measuring, 72–73
  natural forces at, 71
  unit of, 72
work input, 84
work output, 84

X

X-ray machine, 65
X-rays, 64–65

Photo Credits

Photography Credits: All photographs are by the Pearson Learning Group (PLG), John Serafin for PLG, and David Mager for PLG, except as noted below.

Cover: *bkgd.* Alan Schein Photography/Corbis; *inset* SuperStock, Inc.

Table of Contents: iv Tom Twomey/Check Six; v Peter Hayman/British Museum/Dorling Kindersley Limited

Frontmatter: P001 bl CityNet Telecom; P001 bm John Sohlden/Visuals Unlimited, Inc.; P001 tr Gregg Otto/Visuals Unlimited, Inc.; P002 l Bernd Wittich/Visuals Unlimited, Inc.; P001Stock Trek/PhotoDisc, Inc.; P002 m Charles O'Rear/Corbis; P003 Stock Trek/PhotoDisc, Inc.; P005 r Stock Trek/PhotoDisc, Inc.; P007 r Stock Trek/PhotoDisc, Inc.; P009 r Stock Trek/PhotoDisc, Inc.; P009 mr Larry Mulvehill/Photo Researchers, Inc.; P009 t Jay Freis/Image Bank; P009 tr Ed Young/Corbis; P011 r Stock Trek/PhotoDisc, Inc.; P013 r Stock Trek/PhotoDisc, Inc.

Chapter 1: P15 Grantpix/Photo Researchers, Inc.; P18 J-L Charmet/Science Photo Library/Photo Researchers, Inc.; P19 Tom Twomey/Check Six; P22 Larry Lefever/Grant Heilman Photography, Inc.; P24 Patrick Behar/Photo Researchers, Inc.; P27 b Bruce M. Wellman/ Stock, Boston, Inc.; P27 t Bob Daemmrich Photos/Stock, Boston Inc.; P29 John Elk, III/Bruce Coleman, Inc.; P34 Eric Neurath/Stock, Boston Inc.; P38 Grantpix/Photo Researchers, Inc.; P39 Grantpix/Photo Researchers, Inc.; P40 Grantpix/Photo Researchers, Inc.

Chapter 2: P41 E. R. Degginger/Animals Animals/Earth Scenes; P42 Leonard Lessin/Peter Arnold, Inc.; P44 Fotopic/Omni-Photo Communications; P46 Peter Sherrard/FPG; P47 Tim Fitzharris/ Minden Pictures; P48 Johnny Cann doubling for Chuck Norris on "Walker Texas Ranger." Photo by Roy Empfield, property of Action P.A.C. Stunts, L.L.C./Action Pac; P49 b Insurance Institute for Highway Safety; P49 m Energy Absorption Systems, Inc.; P49 t Science VU/Visuals Unlimited, Inc.; P50 b Bettmann/Corbis; P51 George & Judy Manna/Photo Researchers, Inc.; P53 The Granger Collection, New York/The Granger Collection; P54 l PhotoDisc, Inc./PhotoDisc; P54 r Kevin Morris/Getty Images; P55 Mike Phillips/Peter Arnold, Inc.; P58 E. R. Degginger/Animals Animals/Earth Scenes; P59 E. R. Degginger/Animals Animals/Earth Scenes; P60 E. R. Degginger/Animals Animals/Earth Scenes

Chapter 3: P61 Neil Rabinowitz/Corbis; P62 inset Michael Matisse/PhotoDisc, Inc.; P62 l Walter H. Hodge/Peter Arnold, Inc.; P62 r Bill Ross/Corbis; P63 b C. C. Lockwood/Animals Animals/Earth Scenes; P63 t AP/Wide World Photos; P64 Johnny Johnson/Animals Animals/Earth Scenes; P65 Will & Deni McIntyre/Photo Researchers, Inc.; P66 Gary S. Settles/Photo Researchers, Inc.; P67 NOAO/ Science Photo Library/Photo Researchers, Inc.; P67 inset LOC/Science Source/Photo Researchers, Inc.; P68 t Simon Fraser/Science Photo Library/Photo Researchers, Inc.; P68-69 b Amos Zezmer/Omni-Photo Communications; P69 inset Billie Johnson/United States Corps. of Engineers, Washington; P69 tl Adam Jones/Photo Researchers, Inc.; P69 tr David R. Frazier Photolibrary/Photo Researchers, Inc.; P71 AFP/Corbis; P74 bl Richard Kolar/Animals Animals/Earth Scenes; P74 br Science VU/Visuals Unlimited, Inc.; P74 tl Michael Habicht/Animals Animals/Earth Scenes; P78 Neil Rabinowitz/Corbis; P79 Neil Rabinowitz/Corbis; P80 Neil Rabinowitz/Corbis

Chapter 4: P81 Paolo Koch/Photo Researchers, Inc.; P82 Geostock/PhotoDisc; P84 E. R. Degginger/Color Pic, Inc.; P85 AFP/Corbis; P92 b Esbin/Anderson/Omni-Photo Communications; P92 t Michael Thompson/Animals Animals/Earth Scenes; P94 bl Dorling Kindersley Limited; P94 inset Peter Hayman/British Museum/Dorling Kindersley Limited; P94 t British Museum/Dorling Kindersley Limited; P94-95 Geoff Brightling/Dorling Kindersley Limited; P95 t Daniel Moignot, P.L.J. Gallimard Jeunesse-Larousse/Dorling Kindersley Limited; P96 t Jodi Jacobson/Peter Arnold, Inc.; P97 b CityNet Telecom; P97 t Robin Smith/Getty Images; P98 Paolo Koch/Photo Researchers, Inc.; P99 Paolo Koch/Photo Researchers, Inc.; P100 Paolo Koch/Photo Researchers, Inc.